2.90

• Letter to Nancy
• Dictionary

''

Alpha Thru Epsilon in Greek

$ 250 in Greek
+ Conditionals
+ Plate

\

Under the Editorship of

WILLIAM G. MOULTON, *Princeton University*

THE

Gretchen

Episode

Edited by

R-M. S. HEFFNER *University of Wisconsin*

HELMUT REHDER *University of Texas*

W. F. TWADDELL *Brown University*

FROM

Goethe's Faust

HOUGHTON MIFFLIN COMPANY

FOREWORD

THE GRETCHEN EPISODE from FAUST is a brief and self-contained part of the great poem. Its style and vocabulary present few problems for an American student in the later phases of his elementary study of German — say, the third or fourth semester of the conventional course. Its verse form is simple, and there is a minimum of specifically poetic diction or syntax. Its content is both understandable and important for readers in their late teens and early twenties.

The text follows that of our complete student's edition of FAUST: Parts I and II (D. C. Heath & Co.); the notes are adapted to this episode; the vocabulary aims to be complete.

R–M. S. H.
H. R.
W. F. T.

INTRODUCTION

Johann Wolfgang Goethe (*1749–1832*): The most eminent German man of letters, — novelist, poet, dramatist, essayist. Educated for the law. Government official in the duchy of Saxe-Weimar. Well-informed amateur of the arts. Interested student of the sciences; did considerable independent work in optics, mineralogy, and biology (evolution). As writer and thinker, a major influence on European and American thought since his youthful days.

Faust: Historical figure of the early sixteenth century, a traveling magician, fortune-teller, and magic healer: a notorious charlatan and quack, who died around 1540 somewhat mysteriously.

In popular lore, Faust was believed to have sold his soul to the Devil in return for supernatural powers. By the end of the sixteenth century, a fantastic biography of the famous professor-magician had been published, telling of his impious intellectual ambition, his mastery of magic, and his adventures with the aid of an indentured devil Mephistopheles (high living, debauchery, travels to hell and heaven, visits at Rome and Constantinople and the imperial court, an affair with Helen of Troy). After twenty-four years, Faust's soul is carried off to hell in accordance with the contract.

This legend, in various forms, was widely popular and served as the theme of narratives and dramas (for instance, Christopher Marlowe's *Doctor Faustus*), especially puppet-plays. Both Goethe and his contemporary audience were familiar with the main outlines of the legend.

Goethe's Faust: Goethe uses the familiar Faust-story as a
vehicle for the portrayal of modern man. The theme fascinated
him throughout his long adult life: he planned a Faust-drama as
early as 1770, and he completed the work as we now have it in
1831.

Goethe changes the moral direction of the old story. Faust's
striving for knowledge and experience (which was the essence
of wickedness in the older accounts) becomes in Goethe's formu-
lation the essential quality of humanity, involving error and guilt
and disaster, but even so the source of human progress and human
greatness. Goethe's hero is not carried off to hell; the end of the
work shows Faust beginning a new career of growth and evolution in a dynamic heaven. This characteristic striving and dis-
satisfaction with past achievement has raised Goethe's Faust to
the level of a symbol of modern West European man. Such stu-
dents of cultural history as Spengler (*Decline of the West*) and
Toynbee (*Study of History*) use 'Faust' and 'Faustian' as labels for
our civilization.

The Gretchen Episode is one of several major experiences
through which Faust proceeds in his career on earth. It portrays
the youthful (rejuvenated) Faust in a turmoil of sex. The devel-
opment of the episode is fairly free from supernatural elements.
Faust is a worldly and intelligent and self-centered man; Gretchen
is an attractive, affectionate, conventional small-town girl. Two
such personalities furnish all the ingredients of drama, without
any necessity for the intervention of a devil. To be sure,
Mephistopheles is active in furthering the affair and in over-
coming Faust's scruples. But he contributes no help which
Faust himself could not have supplied, though at some incon-
venience. And Mephistopheles' incitements, his deadening of
Faust's conscience, are only an external representation of Faust's
own drives. After all, Faust is a less exceptional hero in the
Gretchen episode than in any of the other major adventures; his

behavior with Gretchen is explicable in terms of not very uncommon human traits.

And it is thus that Goethe presents him: a strong human being involved by his erotic urges in a situation which places heavy demands on his wisdom and his respect for another human being — heavier demands than he can meet. He fails, and his failure is a catastrophe.

In the larger setting of the total FAUST, the Gretchen episode is one of the failures from which Faust emerges, wounded and bruised and chastened, but yet with powers of recuperation and resources of energy to try again, to strive further, to harness discontent and remorse in the service of new exertion.

Faust

PART ONE

In a Prolog in Heaven, *God and Mephistopheles discuss Faust. Mephistopheles portrays Faust as a rebel against the divinely-ordained limitations upon human knowledge and experience. God claims Faust as His servant, despite the errors and confusions which are inescapable for human beings. Mephistopheles wagers that he can capture Faust's soul by making him a willing follower of the Devil's path. God is not only confident of Faust's essential goodness; God even asserts that Mephistopheles' assaults on human souls keep men alert and active and dissatisfied, and thus serve God's purpose.*

Faust is shown in his study, alone, late at night, reviewing his disappointing status in life. He has followed the conventional paths of study and has achieved the outward trappings of conventional success: he is acknowledged as a man of great learning, a leading professor. But he is dissatisfied with the superficial nature of his knowledge and bored with his attempts to teach. He resolves to resort to magic. He succeeds in evoking some spirit manifestations; but the Earth-spirit repulses him as incapable of coping with creative spirits. Faust, despairing of ever satisfying

2 Faust, Part One

his intellectual cravings, decides to commit suicide. He is restrained by the sound of Easter bells and choruses. Although he no longer believes in their message of redemption and hope, the habit of faith from his childhood years holds him back from the irrevocable act of self-destruction.

Mephistopheles appears in Faust's study the next night, and hints at his power to satisfy Faust's desires. On a later visit, Mephistopheles proposes a simple exchange of services: Mephistopheles will serve Faust on this earth, Faust will serve Mephistopheles in the next world. Faust is contemptuous of the value of Mephistopheles' services; he doubts whether a devil's arts can satisfy an honest human being's deepest striving. For an honest man's striving is for more than mere pleasure: it is for significant experience, pain as well as happiness, suffering as well as joy. Faust proposes a contract based specifically on the value of the devil's offerings: If Faust can ever be completely satisfied, if Mephistopheles can make any one single instant so significant that Faust would wish that moment to last forever — then Faust will have lost; he will be willing to die, and it makes no difference to him whose servant (if anyone's) he is thereafter. Mephistopheles accepts these terms and prepares to escort Faust through such variegated experiences as no human being has had before.

One step in Mephistopheles' curriculum for Faust is accomplished in the Witch's Kitchen: the witch gives Faust a drink which rejuvenates him and gives him a young man's capacity and unreflecting desire for experience. Faust emerges from the Witch's Kitchen with the appetites of a youth. He catches sight of a girl walking home from church . . .

9

Straße

Faust. Margarete vorübergehend.

FAUST

2605 Mein schönes Fräulein! Darf ich wagen,
Meinen Arm und Geleit Ihr anzutragen?

MARGARETE

Bin weder Fräulein, weder schön.
Kann ungeleitet nach Hause gehn.

Sie macht sich los und ab.

FAUST

Beim Himmel, dieses Kind ist schön!

2610 So etwas hab' ich nie gesehn.
Sie ist so sitt- und tugendreich,
Und etwas schnippisch doch zugleich.
Der Lippe Rot, der Wange Licht,
Die Tage der Welt vergess' ich's nicht!

2615 Wie sie die Augen niederschlägt,
Hat tief sich in mein Herz geprägt;
Wie sie kurz angebunden war,
Das ist nun zum Entzücken gar!

Mephistopheles tritt auf.

FAUST

Hör, du mußt mir die Dirne schaffen!

NOTES: 2605, 2606, 2607, 2619

MEPHISTOPHELES
2620 Nun, welche?
FAUST
        Sie ging just vorbei.
MEPHISTOPHELES
Da die? Sie kam von ihrem Pfaffen,
Der sprach sie aller Sünden frei:
— Ich schlich mich hart am Stuhl vorbei. —
Es ist ein gar unschuldig Ding,
2625 Das eben für nichts zur Beichte ging:
Über die hab' ich keine Gewalt.
FAUST
Ist über vierzehn Jahr doch alt.
MEPHISTOPHELES
Du sprichst ja wie Hans Liederlich:
Der begehrt jede liebe Blum' für sich,
2630 Und dünkelt ihm, es wär' kein' Ehr'
Und Gunst, die nicht zu pflücken wär':
Geht aber doch nicht immer an.
FAUST
Mein Herr Magister Lobesan,
Lass' Er mich mit dem Gesetz in Frieden!
2635 Und das sag' ich Ihm kurz und gut:
Wenn nicht das süße junge Blut
Heut nacht in meinen Armen ruht,
So sind wir um Mitternacht geschieden.
MEPHISTOPHELES
Bedenkt, was gehn und stehen mag!
2640 Ich brauche wenigstens vierzehn Tag',
Nur die Gelegenheit auszuspüren.

NOTES: 2624, 2627, 2628, 2630, 2633, 2634, 2639

FAUST

Hätt' ich nur sieben Stunden Ruh,
Brauchte den Teufel nicht dazu,
So ein Geschöpfchen zu verführen.

MEPHISTOPHELES

2645 Ihr sprecht schon fast wie ein Franzos!
Doch bitt' ich, laßt's Euch nicht verdrießen:
Was hilft's, nur grade zu genießen?
Die Freud' ist lange nicht so groß,
Als wenn Ihr erst herauf, herum,
2650 Durch allerlei Brimborium,
Das Püppchen geknetet und zugericht't,
Wie's lehret manche welsche Geschicht'.

FAUST

Hab' Appetit auch ohne das.

MEPHISTOPHELES

Jetzt ohne Schimpf und ohne Spaß!
2655 Ich sag' Euch: mit dem schönen Kind
Geht's ein für allemal nicht geschwind.
Mit Sturm ist da nichts einzunehmen;
Wir müssen uns zur List bequemen.

FAUST

Schaff mir etwas vom Engelsschatz!
2660 Führ mich an ihren Ruheplatz!
Schaff mir ein Halstuch von ihrer Brust,
Ein Strumpfband meiner Liebeslust!

MEPHISTOPHELES

Damit Ihr seht, daß ich Eurer Pein
Will förderlich und dienstlich sein,
2665 Wollen wir keinen Augenblick verlieren;
Will Euch noch heut in ihr Zimmer führen.

FAUST

Und soll sie sehn, — sie haben?

MEPHISTOPHELES

                    Nein!

NOTES: 2645, 2651, 2652, 2654

Sie wird bei einer Nachbarin sein.
Indessen könnt Ihr ganz allein
267c An aller Hoffnung künft'ger Freuden
In ihrem Dunstkreis satt Euch weiden.

FAUST
Können wir hin?

MEPHISTOPHELES
Es ist noch zu früh.

FAUST
Sorg du mir für ein Geschenk für sie!

Ab.

MEPHISTOPHELES
Gleich schenken? Das ist brav! Da wird er reüssieren!
2675 Ich kenne manchen schönen Platz
Und manchen altvergrabnen Schatz;
Ich muß ein bißchen revidieren.

Ab.

NOTES: 2674, 2675

10

Abend

Ein kleines, reinliches Zimmer.
Margarete, ihre Zöpfe flechtend und aufbindend.

MARGARETE
Ich gäb' was drum, wenn ich nur wüßt',
Wer heut der Herr gewesen ist!
2680 Er sah gewiß recht wacker aus
Und ist aus einem edlen Haus;
Das konnt' ich ihm an der Stirne lesen —
Er wär' auch sonst nicht so keck gewesen.
Ab.
Mephistopheles und Faust treten auf.

MEPHISTOPHELES
Herein, ganz leise, nur herein!
FAUST, *nach einigem Stillschweigen.*
2685 Ich bitte dich, laß mich allein!
MEPHISTOPHELES, *herumspürend.*
Nicht jedes Mädchen hält so rein.
Ab.
FAUST, *rings aufschauend.*
Willkommen, süßer Dämmerschein,
Der du dies Heiligtum durchwebst!
Ergreif mein Herz, du süße Liebespein,
2690 Die du vom Tau der Hoffnung schmachtend lebst!

NOTES: Scene 10; 2683, 2688

7

Wie atmet rings Gefühl der Stille,
Der Ordnung, der Zufriedenheit! –
In dieser Armut welche Fülle!
In diesem Kerker welche Seligkeit!
Er wirft sich auf den ledernen Sessel am Bette.

2695 O nimm mich auf, der du die Vorwelt schon
Bei Freud' und Schmerz im offnen Arm empfangen!
Wie oft, ach, hat an diesem Väterthron
Schon eine Schar von Kindern rings gehangen!
Vielleicht hat, dankbar für den heil'gen Christ,

2700 Mein Liebchen hier, mit vollen Kinderwangen,
Dem Ahnherrn fromm die welke Hand geküßt.
Ich fühl', o Mädchen, deinen Geist
Der Füll' und Ordnung um mich säuseln,
Der mütterlich dich täglich unterweist,

2705 Den Teppich auf den Tisch dich reinlich breiten heißt,
Sogar den Sand zu deinen Füßen kräuseln.
O liebe Hand, so göttergleich!
Die Hütte wird durch dich ein Himmelreich.
Und hier! . . .
Er hebt einen Bettvorhang auf.
          Was faßt mich für ein Wonnegraus!

2710 Hier möcht' ich volle Stunden säumen.
Natur, hier bildetest in leichten Träumen
Den eingebornen Engel aus!
Hier lag das Kind, mit warmem Leben
Den zarten Busen angefüllt;

2715 Und hier mit heilig reinem Weben
Entwirkte sich das Götterbild!
Und du! Was hat dich hergeführt?
Wie innig fühl' ich mich gerührt!
Was willst du hier? Was wird das Herz dir schwer?

2720 Armsel'ger Faust! Ich kenne dich nicht mehr.
Umgibt mich hier ein Zauberduft?
Mich drang's, so grade zu genießen,

NOTES: 2694, 2696, 2706, 2708, 2711, 2712, 2714, 2715, 2720

Und fühle mich in Liebestraum zerfließen!
Sind wir ein Spiel von jedem Druck der Luft?

2725 Und träte sie den Augenblick herein,
Wie würdest du für deinen Frevel büßen!
Der große Hans, ach, wie so klein,
Läg', hingeschmolzen, ihr zu Füßen.

Mephistopheles kommt.

MEPHISTOPHELES
Geschwind! Ich seh' sie unten kommen.

FAUST
2730 Fort! Fort! Ich kehre nimmermehr!

MEPHISTOPHELES
Hier ist ein Kästchen leidlich schwer.
Ich hab's woanders hergenommen.
Stellt's hier nur immer in den Schrein!
Ich schwör' Euch, ihr vergehn die Sinnen;
2735 Ich tat Euch Sächelchen hinein,
Um eine andre zu gewinnen.
Zwar Kind ist Kind, und Spiel ist Spiel.

FAUST
Ich weiß nicht, soll ich?

MEPHISTOPHELES
Fragt Ihr viel?
Meint Ihr vielleicht den Schatz zu wahren?
2740 Dann rat' ich Eurer Lüsternheit,
Die liebe schöne Tageszeit
Und mir die weitre Müh' zu sparen.
Ich hoff' nicht, daß Ihr geizig seid!
Ich kratz' den Kopf, reib' an den Händen,—

*Er stellt das Kästchen in den Schrein und drückt das Schloß
wieder zu.*

2745 — Nur fort! Geschwind! —
Um Euch das süße junge Kind
Nach Herzens Wunsch und Will' zu wenden;
Und Ihr seht drein,

NOTES: 2732, 2736, 2737, 2738, 2739, 2740, 2744

Als solltet Ihr in den Hörsaal hinein,
2750 Als stünden grau leibhaftig vor Euch da
Physik und Metaphysika!
Nur fort!

Ab.

Margarete mit einer Lampe.

MARGARETE
Es ist so schwül, so dumpfig hie ...

Sie macht das Fenster auf.

Und ist doch eben so warm nicht drauß.
2755 Es wird mir so, ich weiß nicht wie —
Ich wollt', die Mutter käm' nach Haus!
Mir läuft ein Schauer übern ganzen Leib
Bin doch ein töricht-furchtsam Weib!

Sie fängt an zu singen, indem sie sich auszieht.

Es war ein König in Thule,
2760 Gar treu bis an das Grab,
Dem sterbend seine Buhle
Einen goldnen Becher gab.

Es ging ihm nichts darüber,
Er leert' ihn jeden Schmaus;
2765 Die Augen gingen ihm über,
So oft er trank daraus.

Und als er kam zu sterben,
Zählt' er seine Städt' im Reich,
Gönnt' alles seinen Erben,
2770 Den Becher nicht zugleich.

Er saß beim Königsmahle,
Die Ritter um ihn her,
Auf hohem Vätersaale,
Dort, auf dem Schloß am Meer.

NOTES: 2751, 2753, 2758, 2759, 2761

2775 Dort stand der alte Zecher,
Trank letzte Lebensglut
Und warf den heiligen Becher
Hinunter in die Flut.

Er sah ihn stürzen, trinken
2780 Und sinken tief ins Meer.
Die Augen täten ihm sinken,
Trank nie einen Tropfen mehr.

Sie eröffnet den Schrein, ihre Kleider einzuräumen, und erblickt
das Schmuckkästchen.
Wie kommt das schöne Kästchen hier herein?
Ich schloß doch ganz gewiß den Schrein.
2785 Es ist doch wunderbar! Was mag wohl drinne sein?
Vielleicht bracht's jemand als ein Pfand,
Und meine Mutter lieh darauf.
Da hängt ein Schlüsselchen am Band,
Ich denke wohl, ich mach' es auf! —
2790 Was ist das? Gott im Himmel! Schau!
So was hab' ich mein' Tage nicht gesehn!
Ein Schmuck! Mit dem könnt' eine Edelfrau
Am höchsten Feiertage gehn. —
Wie sollte mir die Kette stehn?
2795 Wem mag die Herrlichkeit gehören?
Sie putzt sich damit auf und tritt vor den Spiegel.
Wenn nur die Ohrring' meine wären!
Man sieht doch gleich ganz anders drein.
Was hilft Euch Schönheit, junges Blut?
Das ist wohl alles schön und gut,
2800 Allein man läßt's auch alles sein;
Man lobt Euch halb mit Erbarmen —
Nach Golde drängt,
Am Golde hängt
Doch alles. Ach, wir Armen!

NOTES: 2775, 2781, 2786, 2800

11

Spaziergang

Faust in Gedanken auf und ab gehend. Zu ihm Mephistopheles.

MEPHISTOPHELES

2805 Bei aller verschmähten Liebe! Beim höllischen Elemente!—
Ich wollt', ich wüßte was Ärger's, daß ich's fluchen könnte!

FAUST

Was hast? Was kneipt dich denn so sehr?
So kein Gesicht sah ich in meinem Leben!

MEPHISTOPHELES

Ich möcht' mich gleich dem Teufel übergeben,
2810 Wenn ich nur selbst kein Teufel wär'!

FAUST

Hat sich dir was im Kopf verschoben?
Dich kleidet's, wie ein Rasender zu toben!

MEPHISTOPHELES

Denkt nur! Den Schmuck, für Gretchen angeschafft,
Den hat ein Pfaff hinweggerafft!
2815 Die Mutter kriegt das Ding zu schauen,
Gleich fängt's ihr heimlich an zu grauen,
Die Frau hat gar einen feinen Geruch,
Schnuffelt immer im Gebetbuch
Und riecht's einem jeden Möbel an,
2820 Ob das Ding heilig ist oder profan.

NOTES: Scene 11; 2805, 2807, 2808, 2812, 2814, 2817

Und an dem Schmuck, da spürt sie's klar,
Daß dabei nicht viel Segen war.
„Mein Kind," rief sie, „ungerechtes Gut
Befängt die Seele, zehrt auf das Blut.
2825 Wollen's der Mutter Gottes weihen,
Wird uns mit Himmelsmanna erfreuen."
Margretlein zog ein schiefes Maul.
„Ist halt," dacht' sie, „ein geschenkter Gaul,
Und wahrlich, gottlos ist nicht der,
2830 Der ihn so fein gebracht hierher."
Die Mutter ließ einen Pfaffen kommen.
Der hatte kaum den Spaß vernommen,
Ließ sich den Anblick wohl behagen.
Er sprach: „So ist man recht gesinnt!
2835 Wer überwindet, der gewinnt.
Die Kirche hat einen guten Magen,
Hat ganze Länder aufgefressen
Und doch noch nie sich übergessen.
Die Kirch' allein, meine lieben Frauen,
2840 Kann ungerechtes Gut verdauen."
    FAUST
Das ist ein allgemeiner Brauch,
Ein Jud' und König kann es auch.
    MEPHISTOPHELES
Strich drauf ein Spange, Kett' und Ring',
Als wären's eben Pfifferling';
2845 Dankt' nicht weniger und nicht mehr,
Als ob's ein Korb voll Nüsse wär';
Versprach ihnen allen himmlischen Lohn.
Und sie waren sehr erbaut davon.
    FAUST
Und Gretchen?
    MEPHISTOPHELES
        Sitzt nun unruhvoll,
2850 Weiß weder, was sie will noch soll,

NOTES: 2823, 2828, 2830, 2835, 2838, 2843, 2849

Denkt ans Geschmeide Tag und Nacht,
Noch mehr an den, der's ihr gebracht.

FAUST

Des Liebchens Kummer tut mir leid.
Schaff du ihr gleich ein neu Geschmeid'!
2855 Am ersten war ja so nicht viel.

MEPHISTOPHELES

O ja, dem Herrn ist alles Kinderspiel!

FAUST

Und mach, und richt's nach meinem Sinn,
Häng dich an ihre Nachbarin!
Sei Teufel doch nur nicht wie Brei,
2860 Und schaff einen neuen Schmuck herbei!

MEPHISTOPHELES

Ja, gnäd'ger Herr, von Herzen gerne!

Faust ab.

MEPHISTOPHELES

So ein verliebter Tor verpufft
Euch Sonne, Mond und alle Sterne
Zum Zeitvertreib dem Liebchen in die Luft.

Ab.

NOTES: 2851, 2852, 2854, 2857, 2859, 2861, 2863

Der Nachbarin Haus

Marthe allein.

MARTHE

1865 Gott verzeih's meinem lieben Mann:
Er hat an mir nicht wohl getan!
Geht da stracks in die Welt hinein
Und läßt mich auf dem Stroh allein.
Tät ihn doch wahrlich nicht betrüben,
1870 Tät ihn, weiß Gott, recht herzlich lieben . . .
Sie weint.
Vielleicht ist er gar tot! — O Pein! — —
Hätt' ich nur einen Totenschein!

Margarete kommt.

MARGARETE
Frau Marthe!

MARTHE
Gretelchen, was soll's?

MARGARETE
Fast sinken mir die Kniee nieder!
1875 Da find' ich so ein Kästchen wieder
In meinem Schrein! Von Ebenholz!
Und Sachen herrlich ganz und gar!
Weit reicher, als das erste war!

NOTES: Scene 12; 2868, 2869, 2872, 2873

15

MARTHE
Das muß Sie nicht der Mutter sagen;
2880 Tät's wieder gleich zur Beichte tragen.
MARGARETE
Ach seh' Sie nur! Ach schau' Sie nur!
MARTHE *putzt sie auf.*
O du glücksel'ge Kreatur!
MARGARETE
Darf mich, leider, nicht auf der Gassen
Noch in der Kirche mit sehen lassen.
MARTHE
2885 Komm du nur oft zu mir herüber,
Und leg den Schmuck hier heimlich an!
Spazier ein Stündchen lang dem Spiegelglas vorüber;
Wir haben unsre Freude dran.
Und dann gibt's einen Anlaß, gibt's ein Fest,
2890 Wo man's so nach und nach den Leuten sehen läßt.
Ein Kettchen erst, die Perle dann ins Ohr;
Die Mutter sieht's wohl nicht, man macht ihr auch
     was vor.
MARGARETE
Wer konnte nur die beiden Kästchen bringen?
Es geht nicht zu mit rechten Dingen!
Es klopft.
MARGARETE
2895 Ach Gott! Mag das meine Mutter sein?
MARTHE, *durchs Vorhängel guckend.*
Es ist ein fremder Herr. — Herein!
Mephistopheles tritt auf.
MEPHISTOPHELES
Bin so frei, grad hereinzutreten,
Muß bei den Frauen Verzeihn erbeten.
     Tritt ehrerbietig vor Margareten zurück.
Wollte nach Frau Marthe Schwerdtlein fragen.

NOTES: 2879, 2880, 2883, 2884, 2889, 2896, 2897

MARTHE

2900 Ich bin's! Was hat der Herr zu sagen?

MEPHISTOPHELES, *leise zu ihr.*

Ich kenne Sie jetzt, mir ist das genug;
Sie hat da gar vornehmen Besuch.
Verzeiht die Freiheit, die ich genommen!
Will nach Mittage wieder kommen.

MARTHE, *laut.*

2905 Denk, Kind! Um alles in der Welt!
Der Herr dich für ein Fräulein hält!

MARGARETE

Ich bin ein armes junges Blut —
Ach Gott! Der Herr ist gar zu gut:
Schmuck und Geschmeide sind nicht mein

MEPHISTOPHELES

2910 Ach, es ist nicht der Schmuck allein;
Sie hat ein Wesen, einen Blick so scharf!
Wie freut mich's, daß ich bleiben darf.

MARTHE

Was bringt Er denn? Verlange sehr —

MEPHISTOPHELES

Ich wollt', ich hätt' eine frohere Mär!
2915 Ich hoffe, Sie läßt mich's drum nicht büßen:
Ihr Mann ist tot und läßt Sie grüßen.

MARTHE

Ist tot? Das treue Herz! O weh!
Mein Mann ist tot! Ach, ich vergeh'!

MARGARETE

Ach, liebe Frau, verzweifelt nicht!

MEPHISTOPHELES

2920 So hört die traurige Geschicht'!

MARGARETE

Ich möchte drum mein' Tag' nicht lieben:
Würde mich Verlust zu Tode betrüben

NOTES: 2902, 2903, 2906, 2911, 2921.

MEPHISTOPHELES
Freud' muß Leid, Leid muß Freude haben.

MARTHE
Erzählt mir seines Lebens Schluß!

MEPHISTOPHELES
2925 Er liegt in Padua begraben
Beim heiligen Antonius,
An einer wohlgeweihten Stätte
Zum ewig kühlen Ruhebette.

MARTHE
Habt Ihr sonst nichts an mich zu bringen?

MEPHISTOPHELES
2930 Ja, eine Bitte, groß und schwer:
Lass' Sie doch ja für ihn dreihundert Messen singen! —
Im übrigen sind meine Taschen leer.

MARTHE
Was! Nicht ein Schaustück? Kein Geschmeid'?
Was jeder Handwerksbursch im Grund des Säckels spart,
2935 Zum Angedenken aufbewahrt,
Und lieber hungert, lieber bettelt —

MEPHISTOPHELES
Madam, es tut mir herzlich leid!
Allein er hat sein Geld wahrhaftig nicht verzettelt;
Auch er bereute seine Fehler sehr,
2940 Ja, und bejammerte sein Unglück noch viel mehr.

MARGARETE
Ach, daß die Menschen so unglücklich sind!
Gewiß, ich will für ihn manch Requiem noch beten.

MEPHISTOPHELES
Ihr wäret wert, gleich in die Eh' zu treten:
Ihr seid ein liebenswürdig Kind.

NOTES: 2923, 2926, 2927, 2931, 2943

MARGARETE

2945　Ach nein, das geht jetzt noch nicht an.

MEPHISTOPHELES

Ist's nicht ein Mann, sei's derweil ein Galan.

's ist eine der größten Himmelsgaben,

So ein lieb Ding im Arm zu haben.

MARGARETE

Das ist des Landes nicht der Brauch.

MEPHISTOPHELES

2950　Brauch oder nicht! — Es gibt sich auch!

MARTHE

Erzählt mir doch!

MEPHISTOPHELES

Ich stand an seinem Sterbebette;

Es war was besser als von Mist,

Von halbgefaultem Stroh. Allein er starb als Christ

Und fand, daß er weit mehr noch auf der Zeche hätte.

2955　„Wie," rief er, „muß ich mich von Grund aus hassen,

So mein Gewerb, mein Weib so zu verlassen!

Ach, die Erinnrung tötet mich!

Vergäb' sie mir nur noch in diesem Leben!" —

MARTHE, *weinend.*

Der gute Mann! Ich hab' ihm längst vergeben.

MEPHISTOPHELES

2960　„Allein, weiß Gott, sie war mehr schuld als ich."

MARTHE

Das lügt er! Was! Am Rand des Grabs zu lügen!

MEPHISTOPHELES

Er fabelte gewiß in letzten Zügen,

Wenn ich nur halb ein Kenner bin.

„Ich hatte," sprach er, „nicht zum Zeitvertreib zu

gaffen,

2965　Erst Kinder und dann Brot für sie zu schaffen,

— Und Brot im allerweit'sten Sinn! —

Und konnte nicht einmal mein Teil in Frieden essen."

NOTES: 2946, 2948, 2954

MARTHE

Hat er so aller Treu', so aller Lieb' vergessen,
Der Plackerei bei Tag und Nacht?

MEPHISTOPHELES

2970 Nicht doch! Er hat Euch herzlich dran gedacht.
Er sprach: „Als ich nun weg von Malta ging,
Da betet' ich für Frau und Kinder brünstig.
Uns war denn auch der Himmel günstig,
Daß unser Schiff ein türkisch Fahrzeug fing,
2975 Das einen Schatz des großen Sultans führte.
Da ward der Tapferkeit ihr Lohn,
Und ich empfing denn auch, wie sich's gebührte,
Mein wohlgemeßnes Teil davon."

MARTHE

Ei wie! Ei wo! Hat er's vielleicht vergraben?

MEPHISTOPHELES

2980 Wer weiß, wo nun es die vier Winde haben!
Ein schönes Fräulein nahm sich seiner an,
Als er in Napel fremd umherspazierte;
Sie hat an ihm viel Lieb's und Treu's getan,
Daß er's bis an sein selig Ende spürte.

MARTHE

2985 Der Schelm! Der Dieb an seinen Kindern!
Auch alles Elend, alle Not
Konnt' nicht sein schändlich Leben hindern!

MEPHISTOPHELES

Ja seht! Dafür ist er nun tot!
Wär' ich nun jetzt an Eurem Platze,
2990 Betraurt' ich ihn ein züchtig Jahr,
Visierte dann unterweil nach einem neuen Schatze.

MARTHE

Ach Gott! Wie doch mein erster war,
Find' ich nicht leicht auf dieser Welt den andern!
Es konnte kaum ein herziger Närrchen sein.

NOTES: 2968, 2970, 2974, 2981, 2992

2995 Er liebte nur das allzuviele Wandern,
Und fremde Weiber, und fremden Wein,
Und das verfluchte Würfelspiel!

MEPHISTOPHELES

Nun, nun, so konnt' es gehn und stehen,
Wenn er Euch ungefähr so viel

3000 Von seiner Seite nachgesehen.
Ich schwör' Euch zu: mit dem Beding
Wechselt' ich selbst mit Euch den Ring!

MARTHE

O, es beliebt dem Herrn zu scherzen!

MEPHISTOPHELES, *für sich.*

Nun mach' ich mich beizeiten fort!

3005 Die hielte wohl den Teufel selbst beim Wort.

Zu Gretchen.

Wie steht es denn mit Ihrem Herzen?

MARGARETE

Was meint der Herr damit?

MEPHISTOPHELES, *für sich.*

Du gut's, unschuldig's Kind!

Laut.

Lebt wohl, ihr Fraun!

MARGARETE

Lebt wohl!

MARTHE

O sagt mir doch geschwind!

Ich möchte gern ein Zeugnis haben,

3010 Wo, wie und wann mein Schatz gestorben und begraben.
Ich bin von je der Ordnung Freund gewesen,
Möcht' ihn auch tot im Wochenblättchen lesen.

MEPHISTOPHELES

Ja, gute Frau, durch zweier Zeugen Mund

NOTES: 2998, 3000, 3005, 3007, 3009, 3010, 3013

Wird allerwegs die Wahrheit kund.

3015 Habe noch gar einen feinen Gesellen,
Den will ich Euch vor den Richter stellen.
Ich bring' ihn her.

MARTHE

           O tut das ja!

MEPHISTOPHELES

Und hier die Jungfrau ist auch da? —
Ein braver Knab'! Ist viel gereist,

3020 Fräuleins alle Höflichkeit erweist.

MARGARETE

Müßte vor dem Herren schamrot werden.

MEPHISTOPHELES

Vor keinem Könige der Erden!

MARTHE

Da hinterm Haus in meinem Garten
Wollen wir der Herrn heut abend warten.

NOTES: 3020, 3024

13

[handwritten top margin:] They b. ... not iht. / in' Psychlogy. / Sie werden wohl für die Psychology nicht interessieren.

Straße

Faust. Mephistopheles. *[handwritten: are you making progress?]*

FAUST

3025 Wie ist's? Will's fördern? Will's bald gehn? *[soon]*

MEPHISTOPHELES

Ah bravo! Find' ich Euch in Feuer? *[fire]*
In kurzer Zeit ist Gretchen Euer! *[(she's yours)]*
Heut abend sollt Ihr sie bei Nachbar' Marthen sehn:
Das ist ein Weib wie auserlesen *[woman] [made to order]*
3030 Zum Kuppler- und Zigeunerwesen! *[gypsy goings-on]*

FAUST *[pimp]*

So recht.

MEPHISTOPHELES

Doch wird auch was von uns begehrt. *[desired]*

FAUST

Ein Dienst ist wohl des andern wert. *[service] [worth]*

MEPHISTOPHELES *[valid testimony]*

Wir legen nur ein gültig Zeugnis nieder, *[down]*
Daß ihres Ehherrn ausgereckte Glieder *[husband] [stretched out limbs]*
3035 In Padua an heil'ger Stätte ruhn. *[place] [rest]*

FAUST

Sehr klug! Wir werden erst die Reise machen müssen!

[handwritten: clever!]

NOTES: Scene 13; 3030, 3031

23

MEPHISTOPHELES

Sancta Simplicitas! Darum ist's nicht zu tun;
Bezeugt nur, ohne viel zu wissen!

FAUST

Wenn Er nichts Besser's hat, so ist der Plan zerrissen.

MEPHISTOPHELES

3040 O heil'ger Mann! Da wärt Ihr's nun!
Ist es das erstemal in Eurem Leben,
Daß Ihr falsch Zeugnis abgelegt?
Habt Ihr von Gott, der Welt und was sich drin bewegt,
Vom Menschen, was sich ihm in Kopf und Herzen regt,
3045 Definitionen nicht mit großer Kraft gegeben,
Mit frecher Stirne, kühner Brust?
Und wollt Ihr recht ins Innre gehen,
Habt Ihr davon — Ihr müßt es grad gestehen —
So viel als von Herrn Schwerdtleins Tod gewußt!

FAUST

3050 Du bist und bleibst ein Lügner, ein Sophiste.

MEPHISTOPHELES

Ja, wenn man's nicht ein bißchen tiefer wüßte.
Denn morgen wirst, in allen Ehren,
Das arme Gretchen nicht betören
Und alle Seelenlieb' ihr schwören?

FAUST

3055 Und zwar von Herzen!

MEPHISTOPHELES

            Gut und schön!
Dann wird von ewiger Treu' und Liebe,
Von einzig überallmächt'gem Triebe —
Wird das auch so von Herzen gehn?

FAUST

Laß das! Es wird! — Wenn ich empfinde,
3060 Für das Gefühl, für das Gewühl
Nach Namen suche, keinen finde,
Dann durch die Welt mit allen Sinnen schweife,
Nach allen höchsten Worten greife

NOTES: 3037, 3040, 3050, 3051, 3057

Und diese Glut, von der ich brenne,
3065 Unendlich, ewig, ewig nenne, —
Ist das ein teuflisch Lügenspiel?

MEPHISTOPHELES
Ich hab' doch recht!

FAUST
Hör! Merk dir dies
—Ich bitte dich! — und schone meine Lunge:
Wer recht behalten will und hat nur eine Zunge,
3070 Behält's gewiß.
Und komm, ich hab' des Schwätzens Überdruß,
Denn du hast recht, vorzüglich weil ich muß.

NOTES: 3072

14

Garten

Margarete an Faustens Arm, Marthe mit Mephistopheles
auf und ab spazierend.

MARGARETE
Ich fühl' es wohl, daß mich der Herr nur schont,
Herab sich läßt, mich zu beschämen.
3075 Ein Reisender ist so gewohnt,
Aus Gütigkeit fürliebzunehmen;
Ich weiß zu gut, daß solch erfahrnen Mann
Mein arm Gespräch nicht unterhalten kann.

FAUST
Ein Blick von dir, ein Wort mehr unterhält,
3080 Als alle Weisheit dieser Welt.

Er küßt ihre Hand.

MARGARETE
Inkommodiert Euch nicht! Wie könnt Ihr sie nur küssen?
Sie ist so garstig, ist so rauh!
Was hab' ich nicht schon alles schaffen müssen!
Die Mutter ist gar zu genau.

Gehn vorüber.

MARTHE

3085 Und Ihr, mein Herr, Ihr reist so immer fort?

MEPHISTOPHELES

Ach, daß Gewerb und Pflicht uns dazu treiben!
Mit wie viel Schmerz verläßt man manchen Ort
Und darf doch nun einmal nicht bleiben!

MARTHE

In raschen Jahren geht's wohl an,
3090 So um und um frei durch die Welt zu streifen;
Doch kömmt die böse Zeit heran,
Und sich als Hagestolz allein zum Grab zu schleifen,
Das hat noch keinem wohlgetan.

MEPHISTOPHELES

Mit Grausen seh' ich das von weiten.

MARTHE

3095 Drum, werter Herr, beratet Euch in Zeiten!

Gehn vorüber.

MARGARETE

Ja, aus den Augen, aus dem Sinn!
Die Höflichkeit ist Euch geläufig;
Allein Ihr habt der Freunde häufig,
Sie sind verständiger, als ich bin.

FAUST

3100 O Beste! Glaube, was man so „verständig" nennt,
Ist oft mehr Eitelkeit und Kurzsinn.

MARGARETE

Wie?

FAUST

Ach, daß die Einfalt, daß die Unschuld nie
Sich selbst und ihren heil'gen Wert erkennt!
Daß Demut, Niedrigkeit, die höchsten Gaben
3105 Der liebevoll austeilenden Natur —

MARGARETE

Denkt Ihr an mich ein Augenblickchen nur,
Ich werde Zeit genug an Euch zu denken haben.

NOTES: 3091, 3094

FAUST

Ihr seid wohl viel allein?

MARGARETE

Ja, unsre Wirtschaft ist nur klein,
3110 Und doch will sie versehen sein.
Wir haben keine Magd; muß kochen, fegen, stricken
Und nähn und laufen früh und spat;
Und meine Mutter ist in allen Stücken
So akkurat!
3115   Nicht, daß sie just so sehr sich einzuschränken hat;
Wir könnten uns weit eh'r als andre regen:
Mein Vater hinterließ ein hübsch Vermögen,
Ein Häuschen und ein Gärtchen vor der Stadt.
Doch hab' ich jetzt so ziemlich stille Tage:
3120 Mein Bruder ist Soldat,
Mein Schwesterchen ist tot.
Ich hatte mit dem Kind wohl meine liebe Not;
Doch übernähm' ich gern noch einmal alle Plage,
So lieb war mir das Kind.

FAUST

Ein Engel, wenn dir's glich!

MARGARETE

3125 Ich zog es auf, und herzlich liebt' es mich.
Es war nach meines Vaters Tod geboren.
Die Mutter gaben wir verloren,
So elend wie sie damals lag,
Und sie erholte sich sehr langsam, nach und nach.
3130 Da konnte sie nun nicht dran denken,
Das arme Würmchen selbst zu tränken;
Und so erzog ich's ganz allein,
Mit Milch und Wasser: so ward's mein.
Auf meinem Arm, in meinem Schoß
3135 War's freundlich, zappelte, ward groß.

FAUST

Du hast gewiß das reinste Glück empfunden.

NOTES: 3112, 3118, 3122

14. Garten

MARGARETE

Doch auch gewiß gar manche schwere Stunden.
Des Kleinen Wiege stand zu Nacht
An meinem Bett: es durfte kaum sich regen,
3140 War ich erwacht.
Bald mußt' ich's tränken, bald es zu mir legen,
Bald, wenn's nicht schwieg, vom Bett aufstehn
Und tänzelnd in der Kammer auf und nieder gehn,
Und früh am Tage schon am Waschtrog stehn,
3145 Dann auf dem Markt und an dem Herde sorgen,
Und immer fort wie heut so morgen.
Da geht's, mein Herr, nicht immer mutig zu;
Doch schmeckt dafür das Essen, schmeckt die Ruh.

Gehn vorüber.

MARTHE

Die armen Weiber sind doch übel dran:
3150 Ein Hagestolz ist schwerlich zu bekehren.

MEPHISTOPHELES

Es käme nur auf Euresgleichen an,
Mich eines Bessern zu belehren.

MARTHE

Sagt grad, mein Herr: habt Ihr noch nichts gefunden?
Hat sich das Herz nicht irgendwo gebunden?

MEPHISTOPHELES

3155 Das Sprichwort sagt: „Ein eigner Herd,
Ein braves Weib sind Gold und Perlen wert."

MARTHE

Ich meine: ob Ihr niemals Lust bekommen?

MEPHISTOPHELES

Man hat mich überall recht höflich aufgenommen.

MARTHE

Ich wollte sagen: ward's nie Ernst in Eurem Herzen?

MEPHISTOPHELES

3160 Mit Frauen soll man sich nie unterstehn zu scherzen.

NOTES: 3146, 3147, 3153, 3155

MARTHE

Ach, Ihr versteht mich nicht!

MEPHISTOPHELES

Das tut mir herzlich leid!

Doch ich versteh', — daß Ihr sehr gütig seid.

Gehn vorüber.

FAUST

Du kanntest mich, o kleiner Engel, wieder,
Gleich als ich in den Garten kam?

MARGARETE

3165 Saht Ihr es nicht? Ich schlug die Augen nieder.

FAUST

Und du verzeihst die Freiheit, die ich nahm,
Was sich die Frechheit unterfangen,
Als du jüngst aus dem Dom gegangen?

MARGARETE

Ich war bestürzt! Mir war das nie geschehn;
3170 Es konnte niemand von mir Übel's sagen.
Ach, dacht' ich, hat er in deinem Betragen
Was Freches, Unanständiges gesehn?
Es schien ihn gleich nur anzuwandeln,
Mit dieser Dirne gradehin zu handeln.
3175 Gesteh' ich's doch! Ich wußte nicht, was sich
Zu Eurem Vorteil hier zu regen gleich begonnte;
Allein gewiß, ich war recht bös auf mich,
Daß ich auf Euch nicht böser werden konnte.

FAUST

Süß Liebchen!

MARGARETE

Laßt einmal!

*Sie pflückt eine Sternblume und zupft die Blätter ab, eins nach
dem andern.*

NOTES: 3174, 3176

14. Garten

FAUST

Was soll das? Einen Strauß?

MARGARETE

3180 Nein, es soll nur ein Spiel.

FAUST

Wie?

MARGARETE

Geht! Ihr lacht mich aus.

Sie rupft und murmelt.

FAUST

Was murmelst du?

MARGARETE, *halblaut.*

Er liebt mich — liebt mich nicht —

FAUST

Du holdes Himmelsangesicht!

MARGARETE *fährt fort.*

Liebt mich — Nicht — Liebt mich — Nicht —

Das letzte Blatt ausrupfend, mit holder Freude.

Er liebt mich!

FAUST

Ja, mein Kind! Laß dieses Blumenwort

3185 Dir Götterausspruch sein: er liebt dich!

Verstehst du, was das heißt? Er liebt dich!

Er faßt ihre beiden Hände.

MARGARETE

Mich überläuft's!

FAUST

O schaudre nicht! Laß diesen Blick,

Laß diesen Händedruck dir sagen,

3190 Was unaussprechlich ist:

Sich hinzugeben ganz und eine Wonne

Zu fühlen, die ewig sein muß!

NOTES: 3179

Ewig! — Ihr Ende würde Verzweiflung sein . . .
Nein, kein Ende! Kein Ende!

Margarete drückt ihm die Hände, macht sich los und läuft
weg. Er steht einen Augenblick in Gedanken, dann folgt er ihr.

MARTHE, *kommend.*

3195 Die Nacht bricht an.

MEPHISTOPHELES

Ja, und wir wollen fort.

MARTHE

Ich bät' Euch, länger hier zu bleiben,
Allein es ist ein gar zu böser Ort:
Es ist, als hätte niemand nichts zu treiben
Und nichts zu schaffen,
3200 Als auf des Nachbarn Schritt und Tritt zu gaffen;
Und man kommt ins Gered', wie man sich immer stellt.—
Und unser Pärchen?

MEPHISTOPHELES

Ist den Gang dort aufgeflogen. —
Mutwill'ge Sommervögel!

MARTHE

Er scheint ihr gewogen.

MEPHISTOPHELES

Und sie ihm auch. Das ist der Lauf der Welt.

NOTES: 3198, 3204

15

Ein Gartenhäuschen

Margarete springt herein, steckt sich hinter die Tür, hält die Fingerspitze an die Lippen und guckt durch die Ritze.

MARGARETE

3205 Er kommt!

Faust kommt.

FAUST

    Ach, Schelm, so neckst du mich!

Treff' ich dich!

Er küßt sie.

MARGARETE, *ihn fassend und den Kuß zurückgebend.*

        Bester Mann! Von Herzen lieb' ich dich!

Mephistopheles klopft an.

FAUST, *stampfend.*

Wer da?

MEPHISTOPHELES

  Gut Freund!

FAUST

        Ein Tier!

MEPHISTOPHELES

        Es ist wohl Zeit zu scheiden.

Marthe kommt.

MARTHE

Ja, es ist spät, mein Herr.

FAUST

Darf ich Euch nicht geleiten?

MARGARETE

Die Mutter würde mich . . . Lebt wohl!

FAUST

Muß ich denn gehn?

3210 Lebt wohl!

MARTHE

Ade!

MARGARETE

Auf baldig Wiedersehn!

Faust und Mephistopheles ab.

MARGARETE

Du lieber Gott! Was so ein Mann
Nicht alles, alles denken kann!
Beschämt nur steh' ich vor ihm da
Und sag' zu allen Sachen „Ja.“
3215 Bin doch ein arm unwissend Kind.
Begreife nicht, was er an mir find't.

Ab.

I don't
understand.

NOTES: 3213

16

Wald und Höhle

Faust, Mephistopheles.

*Faust has withdrawn to a forest solitude to commune with
nature. When he examines his responsibility toward Gretchen,
he realizes what the consequences may be if the affair goes further.
Mephistopheles appears; at first he thinks that Faust has re-
verted to the old professorial search for intellectual insight.
Mephistopheles makes it his business to silence the voice of Faust's
conscience and entice him back into the affair with Gretchen,
using ridicule, and argument, and appeals to Faust's pride and
sensuality . . .*

MEPHISTOPHELES

Habt Ihr nun bald das Leben g'nug geführt?
Wie kann's Euch in die Länge freuen?
Es ist wohl gut, daß man's einmal probiert;
Dann aber wieder zu was Neuen!

FAUST

3255   Ich wollt', du hättest mehr zu tun,
Als mich am guten Tag zu plagen.

MEPHISTOPHELES

Nun, nun! Ich lass' dich gerne ruhn;
Du darfst mir's nicht im Ernste sagen.
An dir Gesellen, unhold, barsch und toll,

NOTES: Scene 16; 3251, 3254, 3256, 3258

35

3260 Ist wahrlich wenig zu verlieren.
Den ganzen Tag hat man die Hände voll!
Was ihm gefällt und was man lassen soll,
Kann man dem Herrn nie an der Nase spüren.
FAUST
Das ist so just der rechte Ton!
3265 Er will noch Dank, daß Er mich ennuyiert.
MEPHISTOPHELES
Wie hätt'st du, armer Erdensohn,
Dein Leben ohne mich geführt?
Vom Kribskrabs der Imagination
Hab' ich dich doch auf Zeiten lang kuriert;
3270 Und wär' ich nicht, so wärst du schon
Von diesem Erdball abspaziert.
Was hast du da in Höhlen, Felsenritzen
Dich wie ein Schuhu zu versitzen?
Was schlurfst aus dumpfem Moos und triefendem Gestein,
3275 Wie eine Kröte, Nahrung ein?
Ein schöner, süßer Zeitvertreib!
Dir steckt der Doktor noch im Leib!
FAUST
Verstehst du, was für neue Lebenskraft
Mir dieser Wandel in der Öde schafft?
3280 Ja, würdest du es ahnen können,
Du wärest Teufel g'nug, mein Glück mir nicht zu gönnen.
MEPHISTOPHELES
Ein überirdisches Vergnügen!
In Nacht und Tau auf den Gebirgen liegen,
Und Erd' und Himmel wonniglich umfassen,
3285 Zu einer Gottheit sich aufschwellen lassen,
Der Erde Mark mit Ahnungsdrang durchwühlen,
Alle sechs Tagewerk' im Busen fühlen,
In stolzer Kraft ich weiß nicht was genießen,
Bald liebewonniglich in alles überfließen,
3290 Verschwunden ganz der Erdensohn,

NOTES: 3268, 3274, 3283, 3287

Und dann die hohe Intuition —
Mit einer Gebärde.
Ich darf nicht sagen, wie — zu schließen!
FAUST
Pfui über dich!
MEPHISTOPHELES
       Das will Euch nicht behagen;
Ihr habt das Recht, gesittet ,,Pfui'' zu sagen.
3295 Man darf das nicht vor keuschen Ohren nennen,
Was keusche Herzen nicht entbehren können.
Und kurz und gut, ich gönn' Ihm das Vergnügen,
Gelegentlich sich etwas vorzulügen;
Doch lange hält Er das nicht aus.
3300   Du bist schon wieder abgetrieben
Und, währt es länger, aufgerieben
In Tollheit — oder Angst und Graus.
Genug damit! Dein Liebchen sitzt dadrinne,
Und alles wird ihr eng und trüb.
3305 Du kommst ihr gar nicht aus dem Sinne,
Sie hat dich übermächtig lieb.
Erst kam deine Liebeswut übergeflossen,
Wie vom geschmolznen Schnee ein Bächlein übersteigt;
Du hast sie ihr ins Herz gegossen,
3310 Nun ist dein Bächlein wieder seicht.
Mich dünkt, anstatt in Wäldern zu thronen,
Ließ' es dem großen Herren gut,
Das arme, affenjunge Blut
Für seine Liebe zu belohnen.
3315 Die Zeit wird ihr erbärmlich lang;
Sie steht am Fenster, sieht die Wolken ziehn
Über die alte Stadtmauer hin.
,,Wenn ich ein Vöglein wär'!'' — so geht ihr Gesang
Tage lang, halbe Nächte lang.
3320 Einmal ist sie munter, meist betrübt,
Einmal recht ausgeweint,

NOTES: 3291, 3293, 3294, 3298, 3300, 3303, 3307, 3318

Dann wieder ruhig, wie's scheint, —
Und immer verliebt.
FAUST
Schlange! Schlange!
MEPHISTOPHELES, *für sich.*
3325 Gelt, daß ich dich fange!
FAUST
Verruchter! Hebe dich von hinnen
Und nenne nicht das schöne Weib!
Bring die Begier zu ihrem süßen Leib
Nicht wieder vor die halbverrückten Sinnen!
MEPHISTOPHELES
3330 Was soll es denn? Sie meint, du seist entflohn,
Und halb und halb bist du es schon.
FAUST
Ich bin ihr nah, und wär' ich noch so fern;
Ich kann sie nie vergessen, nie verlieren!
Ja, ich beneide schon den Leib des Herrn,
3335 Wenn ihre Lippen ihn indes berühren.
MEPHISTOPHELES
Gar wohl, mein Freund! Ich hab' Euch oft beneidet
Ums Zwillingspaar, das unter Rosen weidet.
FAUST
Entfliehe, Kuppler!
MEPHISTOPHELES
                      Schön! Ihr schimpft, und ich muß lachen.
Der Gott, der Bub' und Mädchen schuf,
3340 Erkannte gleich den edelsten Beruf,
Auch selbst Gelegenheit zu machen.
Nur fort, es ist ein großer Jammer!
Ihr sollt in Eures Liebchens Kammer,
Nicht etwa in den Tod!
FAUST
3345 Was ist die Himmelsfreud' in ihren Armen!
Laß mich an ihrer Brust erwarmen:
Fühl' ich nicht immer ihre Not?
NOTES: 3324, 3325, 3326, 3329, 3334, 3335, 3337, 3339, 3340

Bin ich der Flüchtling nicht, der Unbehauste,
Der Unmensch ohne Zweck und Ruh,
3350 Der wie ein Wassersturz von Fels' zu Felsen brauste,
Begierig wütend, nach dem Abgrund zu?
Und seitwärts sie, mit kindlich dumpfen Sinnen,
Im Hüttchen auf dem kleinen Alpenfeld,
Und all ihr häusliches Beginnen
3355 Umfangen in der kleinen Welt.
Und ich, der Gottverhaßte,
Hatte nicht genug,
Daß ich die Felsen faßte
Und sie zu Trümmern schlug!
3360 Sie, ihren Frieden mußt' ich untergraben!
Du, Hölle, mußtest dieses Opfer haben!
Hilf, Teufel, mir die Zeit der Angst verkürzen!
Was muß geschehn, mag's gleich geschehn!
Mag ihr Geschick auf mich zusammenstürzen
3365 Und sie mit mir zugrunde gehn!
MEPHISTOPHELES
Wie's wieder siedet, wieder glüht!
Geh ein und tröste sie, du Tor!
Wo so ein Köpfchen keinen Ausgang sieht,
Stellt er sich gleich das Ende vor.
3370 Es lebe, wer sich tapfer hält!
Du bist doch sonst so ziemlich eingeteufelt:
Nichts Abgeschmackter's find' ich auf der Welt
Als einen Teufel, der verzweifelt.

NOTES: 3349, 3352, 3369, 3372

17

Gretchens Stube

Gretchen am Spinnrade, allein.

GRETCHEN

Meine Ruh ist hin,

3375 Mein Herz ist schwer;
Ich finde sie nimmer *never*
Und nimmermehr.

Wo ich ihn nicht hab',
Ist mir das Grab,
3380 Die ganze Welt
Ist mir vergällt. *made bitter*

Mein armer Kopf
Ist mir verrückt, *deranged*
Mein armer Sinn
3385 Ist mir zerstückt. *distracted*

Meine Ruh ist hin,
Mein Herz ist schwer;
Ich finde sie nimmer
Und nimmermehr.

NOTES: Scene 17; 3378

40

3390 Nach ihm nur schau' ich
Zum Fenster hinaus,
Nach ihm nur geh' ich
Aus dem Haus.

Sein hoher Gang, *bearing*
3395 Sein' edle Gestalt, → *noble*
Seines Mundes Lächeln,
Seiner Augen Gewalt,

Und seiner Rede
Zauberfluß, A MAGICAL FLUSS
3400 Sein Händedruck — HANDSHAKE
Und ach, sein Kuß!

 Meine Ruh ist hin,
Mein Herz ist schwer;
Ich finde sie nimmer
3405 Und nimmermehr.
 heart
Mein Busen drängt *yearns to be with him*
Sich nach ihm hin.
Ach, dürft' ich fassen
Und halten ihn

3410 Und küssen ihn,
So wie ich wollt',
An seinen Küssen
Vergehen sollt'!

 I swoon

18

Marthens Garten

Margarete, Faust.

MARGARETE
Versprich mir, Heinrich! *promise*

FAUST
Was ich kann!

MARGARETE
3415 Nun sag: wie hast du's mit der Religion?
Du bist ein herzlich guter Mann,
Allein ich glaub', du hältst nicht viel davon. *think . of it.*

FAUST
Laß das, mein Kind! Du fühlst, ich bin dir gut;
Für meine Lieben ließ' ich Leib und Blut,
3420 Will niemand sein Gefühl und seine Kirche rauben *steal*

MARGARETE
Das ist nicht recht, man muß dran glauben!

FAUST
Muß man?

MARGARETE
Ach, wenn ich etwas auf dich könnte! *for you*
Du ehrst auch nicht die heil'gen Sakramente!– *honor*

FAUST
Ich ehre sie.

NOTES: Scene 18; 3414, 3415, 3422
42

MARGARETE
    Doch ohne Verlangen!
3425 Zur Messe, zur Beichte bist du lange nicht gegangen.
Glaubst du an Gott?

FAUST
        Mein Liebchen, wer darf sagen:
„Ich glaub' an Gott"?
Magst Priester oder Weise fragen,
Und ihre Antwort scheint nur Spott
3430 Über den Frager zu sein.

MARGARETE
        So glaubst du nicht?

FAUST
Mißhör mich nicht, du holdes Angesicht!
Wer darf ihn nennen
Und wer bekennen:
„Ich glaub' ihn"—
3435 Wer empfinden
Und sich unterwinden
Zu sagen: „Ich glaub' ihn nicht"?
Der Allumfasser,
Der Allerhalter,
3440 Faßt und erhält er nicht
Dich, mich, sich selbst?
Wölbt sich der Himmel nicht da droben?
Liegt die Erde nicht hier unten fest?
Und steigen freundlich blickend
3445 Ewige Sterne nicht herauf?
Schau' ich nicht Aug' in Auge dir?
Und drängt nicht alles
Nach Haupt und Herzen dir
Und webt in ewigem Geheimnis
3450 Unsichtbar sichtbar neben dir?
Erfüll davon dein Herz, so groß es ist!
Und wenn du ganz in dem Gefühle selig bist,
Nenn es dann, wie du willst,
NOTES: 3428, 3429, 3432, 3447, 3451

Nenn's Glück! Herz! Liebe! Gott!
3455 Ich habe keinen Namen
Dafür! Gefühl ist alles,
Name ist Schall und Rauch,
Umnebelnd Himmelsglut.
    MARGARETE
Das ist alles recht schön und gut.
3460 Ungefähr sagt das der Pfarrer auch,
Nur mit ein bißchen andern Worten.
    FAUST
Es sagen's allerorten
Alle Herzen unter dem himmlischen Tage,
Jedes in seiner Sprache:
3465 Warum nicht ich in der meinen?
    MARGARETE
Wenn man's so hört, möcht's leidlich scheinen,
Steht aber doch immer schief darum;
Denn du hast kein Christentum.
    FAUST
Lieb's Kind!
    MARGARETE
        Es tut mir lang schon weh,
3470 Daß ich dich in d e r Gesellschaft seh'.
    FAUST
Wieso?
    MARGARETE
    Der Mensch, den du da bei dir hast,
Ist mir in tiefer, innrer Seele verhaßt!
Es hat mir in meinem Leben
So nichts einen Stich ins Herz gegeben,
3475 Als des Menschen widrig Gesicht.
    FAUST
Liebe Puppe, fürcht ihn nicht!

NOTES: 3456, 3460, 3463, 3470, 3475

MARGARETE

Seine Gegenwart bewegt mir das Blut.

Ich bin sonst allen Menschen gut;

Aber wie ich mich sehne, dich zu schauen,

3480 Hab' ich vor dem Menschen ein heimlich Grauen,

Und halt' ihn für einen Schelm dazu!

Gott verzeih' mir's, wenn ich ihm Unrecht tu'!

FAUST

Es muß auch solche Käuze geben.

MARGARETE

Wollte nicht mit seinesgleichen leben!

3485 Kommt er einmal zur Tür herein,

Sieht er immer so spöttisch drein

Und halb ergrimmt;

Man sieht, daß er an nichts keinen Anteil nimmt.

Es steht ihm an der Stirn geschrieben,

3490 Daß er nicht mag eine Seele lieben.

Mir wird's so wohl in deinem Arm,

So frei, so hingegeben warm,

Und seine Gegenwart schnürt mir das Innre zu.

FAUST

Du ahnungsvoller Engel du!

MARGARETE

3495 Das übermannt mich so sehr,

Daß, wo er nur mag zu uns treten,

Mein' ich sogar, ich liebte dich nicht mehr!

Auch, wenn er da ist, könnt' ich nimmer beten,

Und das frißt mir ins Herz hinein;

3500 Dir, Heinrich, muß es auch so sein.

FAUST

Du hast nun die Antipathie!

MARGARETE

Ich muß nun fort.

FAUST

       Ach, kann ich nie

Ein Stündchen ruhig dir am Busen hängen

Und Brust an Brust und Seel' in Seele drängen?

NOTES: 3480, 3488, 3490, 3492, 3494, 3496, 3498, 3501

MARGARETE

3505 Ach, wenn ich nur alleine schlief'!
Ich ließ' dir gern heut nacht den Riegel offen.
Doch meine Mutter schläft nicht tief,
Und würden wir von ihr betroffen,
Ich wär' gleich auf der Stelle tot!

FAUST

3510 Du Engel, das hat keine Not.
Hier ist ein Fläschchen: drei Tropfen nur
In ihren Trank umhüllen
Mit tiefem Schlaf gefällig die Natur.

MARGARETE

Was tu' ich nicht um deinetwillen!
3515 Es wird ihr hoffentlich nicht schaden?

FAUST

Würd' ich sonst, Liebchen, dir es raten?

MARGARETE

Seh' ich dich, bester Mann, nur an,
Weiß nicht, was mich nach deinem Willen treibt;
Ich habe schon so viel für dich getan,
3520 Daß mir zu tun fast nichts mehr übrigbleibt.

Ab.

Mephistopheles tritt auf.

MEPHISTOPHELES

Der Grasaff'! Ist er weg?

FAUST

Hast wieder spioniert?

MEPHISTOPHELES

Ich hab's ausführlich wohl vernommen:
Herr Doktor wurden da katechisiert.
Hoff', es soll Ihnen wohl bekommen!
3525 Die Mädels sind doch sehr interessiert,
Ob einer fromm und schlicht nach altem Brauch.
Sie denken: ,,Duckt er da, folgt er uns eben auch."

NOTES: 3505, 3511, 3512, 3523, 3527

FAUST
Du Ungeheuer siehst nicht ein,
Wie diese treue, liebe Seele —
3530 Von ihrem Glauben voll,
Der ganz allein
Ihr seligmachend ist, — sich heilig quäle,
Daß sie den liebsten Mann verloren halten soll.

MEPHISTOPHELES
Du übersinnlicher sinnlicher Freier,
3535 Ein Mägdelein nasführet dich!

FAUST
Du Spottgeburt von Dreck und Feuer!

MEPHISTOPHELES
Und die Physiognomie versteht sie meisterlich:
In meiner Gegenwart wird's ihr, sie weiß nicht wie
Mein Mäskchen da weissagt verborgnen Sinn;
3540 Sie fühlt, daß ich ganz sicher ein Genie,
Vielleicht wohl gar der Teufel bin. —
Nun, heute nacht — ?

FAUST
         Was geht dich's an?

MEPHISTOPHELES
Hab' ich doch meine Freude dran!

NOTES: 3531, 3534, 3536

19

Am Brunnen

Gretchen und Lieschen, mit Krügen.

LIESCHEN
Hast nichts von Bärbelchen gehört?

GRETCHEN
3545 Kein Wort. Ich komm' gar wenig unter Leute.

LIESCHEN
Gewiß, Sibylle sagt' mir's heute!
Die hat sich endlich auch betört.
Das ist das Vornehmtun!

GRETCHEN
                            Wieso?

LIESCHEN
                                        Es stinkt!
Sie füttert zwei, wenn sie nun ißt und trinkt.

GRETCHEN
3550 Ach!

LIESCHEN
So ist's ihr endlich recht ergangen.
Wie lange hat sie an dem Kerl gehangen!
Das war ein Spazieren,
Auf Dorf und Tanzplatz Führen!
3555 Mußt' überall die Erste sein!
Kurtesiert' ihr immer mit Pastetchen und Wein.

NOTES: Scene 19; 3544, 3545, 3546, 3548

48

Bild't' sich was auf ihre Schönheit ein;
War doch so ehrlos, sich nicht zu schämen,
Geschenke von ihm anzunehmen.
3560 War ein Gekos' und ein Geschleck':
Da ist denn auch das Blümchen weg!

GRETCHEN
Das arme Ding!

LIESCHEN
          Bedauerst sie noch gar!
Wenn unsereins am Spinnen war,
Uns nachts die Mutter nicht hinunterließ,
3565 Stand sie bei ihrem Buhlen süß;
Auf der Türbank und im dunkeln Gang
Ward ihnen keine Stunde zu lang.
Da mag sie denn sich ducken nun,
Im Sünderhemdchen Kirchbuß' tun!

GRETCHEN
3570 Er nimmt sie gewiß zu seiner Frau.

LIESCHEN
Er wär' ein Narr! Ein flinker Jung'
Hat anderwärts noch Luft genung.
Er ist auch fort.

GRETCHEN
          Das ist nicht schön!

LIESCHEN
Kriegt sie ihn, soll's ihr übel gehn:
3575 Das Kränzel reißen die Buben ihr,
Und Häckerling streuen wir vor die Tür!

Ab.

GRETCHEN, *nach Hause gehend.*
Wie konnt' ich sonst so tapfer schmälen,
Wenn tät ein armes Mägdlein fehlen!
Wie konnt' ich über andrer Sünden
3580 Nicht Worte g'nug der Zunge finden!

NOTES: 3560, 3561, 3569, 3572, 3574, 3575, 3576, 3579, 3580

Wie schien mir's schwarz, und schwärzt's noch gar,
Mir's immer doch nicht schwarz g'nug war,
Und segnet' mich und tat so groß, —
Und bin nun selbst der Sünde bloß!

3585   Doch — alles, was dazu mich trieb,
Gott! war so gut — ach, war so lieb!

20

Zwinger

In der Mauerhöhle ein Andachtsbild der Mater dolorosa, *Blumenkrüge davor. Gretchen steckt frische Blumen in die Krüge.*

GRETCHEN

Ach neige,
Du Schmerzenreiche,
Dein Antlitz gnädig meiner Not!

3590 Das Schwert im Herzen,
Mit tausend Schmerzen
Blickst auf zu deines Sohnes Tod.

Zum Vater blickst du,
Und Seufzer schickst du
3595 Hinauf um sein' und deine Not.

Wer fühlet,
Wie wühlet
Der Schmerz mir im Gebein?
Was mein armes Herz hier banget,
3600 Was es zittert, was verlanget,
Weißt nur du, nur du allein!

Wohin ich immer gehe,
Wie weh, wie weh, wie wehe
Wird mir im Busen hier!
3605 Ich bin, ach, kaum alleine,
Ich wein', ich wein', ich weine,
Das Herz zerbricht in mir.

Die Scherben vor meinem Fenster
Betaut' ich mit Tränen, ach!
3610 Als ich am frühen Morgen
Dir diese Blumen brach.

Schien hell in meine Kammer
Die Sonne früh herauf,
Saß ich in allem Jammer
3615 In meinem Bett schon auf.

Hilf! Rette mich von Schmach und Tod!
Ach neige,
Du Schmerzenreiche,
Dein Antlitz gnädig meiner Not!

NOTES: 3599, 3605, 3608

21

Nacht

Straße vor Gretchens Türe.
Valentin, Soldat, Gretchens Bruder.

VALENTIN

3620   Wenn ich so saß bei einem Gelag,
Wo mancher sich berühmen mag,
Und die Gesellen mir den Flor
Der Mägdlein laut gepriesen vor,
Mit vollem Glas das Lob verschwemmt,
3625   Den Ellenbogen aufgestemmt,
Saß ich in meiner sichern Ruh,
Hört' all dem Schwadronieren zu
Und streiche lächelnd meinen Bart
Und kriege das volle Glas zur Hand
3630   Und sage: „Alles nach seiner Art!
Aber ist e i n e im ganzen Land,
Die meiner trauten Gretel gleicht,
Die meiner Schwester das Wasser reicht?"
Topp! Topp! Kling! Klang! Das ging herum;
3635   Die einen schrieen: „Er hat recht,
Sie ist die Zier vom ganzen Geschlecht!"
Da saßen alle die Lober stumm.
Und nun, — um 's Haar sich auszuraufen
Und an den Wänden hinaufzulaufen! —

NOTES: Scene 21; 3621, 3624, 3625, 3633, 3637, 3638

53

3640 Mit Stichelreden, Naserümpfen
     Soll jeder Schurke mich beschimpfen!
     Soll wie ein böser Schuldner sitzen,
     Bei jedem Zufallswörtchen schwitzen!
     Und möcht' ich sie zusammenschmeißen,
3645 Könnt' ich sie doch nicht Lügner heißen.

       Was kommt heran? Was schleicht herbei?
       Irr' ich nicht, es sind ihrer zwei.
       Ist er's, gleich pack ich ihn beim Felle,
       Soll nicht lebendig von der Stelle!
       Faust und Mephistopheles treten auf.

       FAUST
3650 Wie von dem Fenster dort der Sakristei
     Aufwärts der Schein des ew'gen Lämpchens flämmert
     Und schwach und schwächer seitwärts dämmert,
     Und Finsternis drängt ringsum bei!
     So sieht's in meinem Busen nächtig.

       MEPHISTOPHELES
3655 Und mir ist's wie dem Kätzlein schmächtig,
     Das an den Feuerleitern schleicht,
     Sich leis' dann um die Mauern streicht;
     Mir ist's ganz tugendlich dabei,
     Ein bißchen Diebsgelüst, ein bißchen Rammelei
3660 So spukt mir schon durch alle Glieder
     Die herrliche Walpurgisnacht.
     Die kommt uns übermorgen wieder,
     Da weiß man doch, warum man wacht.

       FAUST
     Rückt wohl der Schatz indessen in die Höh',
3665 Den ich dort hinten flimmern seh'?

       MEPHISTOPHELES
     Du kannst die Freude bald erleben,
     Das Kesselchen herauszuheben.
     Ich schielte neulich so hinein,
     Sind herrliche Löwentaler drein.

       NOTES: 3648, 3650, 3654, 3656, 3658, 3661, 3664

FAUST

3670 Nicht ein Geschmeide, nicht ein Ring,
Meine liebe Buhle damit zu zieren?

MEPHISTOPHELES

Ich sah dabei wohl so ein Ding
Als wie eine Art von Perlenschnüren.

FAUST

So ist es recht! Mir tut es weh,
3675 Wenn ich ohne Geschenke zu ihr geh'.

MEPHISTOPHELES

Es sollt' Euch eben nicht verdrießen,
Umsonst auch etwas zu genießen. —
Jetzt, da der Himmel voller Sterne glüht,
Sollt Ihr ein wahres Kunststück hören:
3680 Ich sing' ihr ein moralisch Lied,
Um sie gewisser zu betören.

Singt zur Zither.

Was machst du mir
Vor Liebchens Tür,
Kathrinchen, hier
3685 Bei frühem Tagesblicke?
Laß, laß es sein!
Er läßt dich ein,
Als Mädchen ein,
Als Mädchen nicht zurücke.

3690 Nehmt euch in acht!
Ist es vollbracht,
Dann gute Nacht,
Ihr armen, armen Dinger!
Habt ihr euch lieb,
3695 Tut keinem Dieb
Nur nichts zulieb',
Als mit dem Ring am Finger!

NOTES: 3673, 3679, 3682, 3684, 3693

VALENTIN *tritt vor.*
Wen lockst du hier? Beim Element!
Vermaledeiter Rattenfänger!
3700 Zum Teufel erst das Instrument!
Zum Teufel hinterdrein den Sänger!
MEPHISTOPHELES
Die Zither ist entzwei! An der ist nichts zu halten.
VALENTIN
Nun soll es an ein Schädelspalten!
MEPHISTOPHELES, *zu Faust.*
Herr Doktor, nicht gewichen! Frisch!
3705 Hart an mich an, wie ich Euch führe!
Heraus mit Eurem Flederwisch!
Nur zugestoßen! Ich pariere.
VALENTIN
Pariere den!
MEPHISTOPHELES
          Warum denn nicht?
VALENTIN
Auch den!
MEPHISTOPHELES
          Gewiß!
VALENTIN
               Ich glaub', der Teufel ficht!
3710 Was ist denn das? Schon wird die Hand mir lahm!
MEPHISTOPHELES, *zu Faust.*
Stoß zu!
VALENTIN *fällt.*
     O weh!
MEPHISTOPHELES
          Nun ist der Lümmel zahm!
Nun aber fort! Wir müssen gleich verschwinden,
Denn schon entsteht ein mörderlich Geschrei.
Ich weiß mich trefflich mit der Polizei,
3715 Doch mit dem Blutbann schlecht mich abzufinden.
Faust und Mephistopheles ab.
NOTES: 3698, 3699, 3703, 3704, 3711, 3714

MARTHE, *am Fenster.*
Heraus! Heraus!
GRETCHEN, *am Fenster.*
Herbei ein Licht!
MARTHE, *wie oben.*
Man schilt und rauft, man schreit und ficht.
VOLK
Da liegt schon einer tot!
MARTHE, *heraustretend.*
Die Mörder, sind sie denn entflohn?
GRETCHEN, *heraustretend.*
3720 Wer liegt hier?
VOLK
Deiner Mutter Sohn!
GRETCHEN
Allmächtiger! Welche Not!
VALENTIN
Ich sterbe! — Das ist bald gesagt
Und bälder noch getan. —
Was steht ihr Weiber, heult und klagt?
3725 Kommt her und hört mich an!
Alle treten um ihn.

Mein Gretchen, sieh! Du bist noch jung,
Bist gar noch nicht gescheit genung,
Machst deine Sachen schlecht.
Ich sag' dir's im Vertrauen nur:
3730 Du bist doch nun einmal eine Hur';
So sei's auch eben recht!
GRETCHEN
Mein Bruder! Gott! Was soll mir das?
VALENTIN
Laß unsern Herrgott aus dem Spaß!
Geschehn ist leider nun geschehn,
3735 Und wie es gehn kann, so wird's gehn.

NOTES: 3720, 3732

Du fingst mit e i n e m heimlich an,
Bald kommen ihrer mehre dran,
Und wenn dich erst ein Dutzend hat,
So hat dich auch die ganze Stadt.
3740 Wenn erst die Schande wird geboren,
Wird sie heimlich zur Welt gebracht,
Und man zieht den Schleier der Nacht
Ihr über Kopf und Ohren;
Ja, man möchte sie gern ermorden.
3745 Wächst sie aber und macht sich groß,
Dann geht sie auch bei Tage bloß
Und ist doch nicht schöner geworden.
Je häßlicher wird ihr Gesicht,
Je mehr sucht sie des Tages Licht.
3750 Ich seh' wahrhaftig schon die Zeit,
Daß alle brave Bürgersleut',
Wie von einer angesteckten Leichen,
Von dir, du Metze, seitab weichen.
Dir soll das Herz im Leib verzagen,
3755 Wenn sie dir in die Augen sehn!
Sollst keine goldne Kette mehr tragen!
In der Kirche nicht mehr am Altar stehn!
In einem schönen Spitzenkragen
Dich nicht beim Tanze wohlbehagen!
3760 In eine finstre Jammerecken
Unter Bettler und Krüppel dich verstecken!
Und wenn dir denn auch Gott verzeiht,
Auf Erden sein vermaledeit!
        MARTHE
Befehlt Eure Seele Gott zu Gnaden!
3765 Wollt Ihr noch Lästrung auf Euch laden?

NOTES: 3737, 3740, 3752, 3754, 3756, 3760, 3765

VALENTIN
Könnt' ich dir nur an den dürren Leib,
Du schändlich kupplerisches Weib,
Da hofft' ich, aller meiner Sünden
Vergebung reiche Maß zu finden!
GRETCHEN
3770 Mein Bruder! Welche Höllenpein!
VALENTIN
Ich sage, laß die Tränen sein!
Da du dich sprachst der Ehre los,
Gabst mir den schwersten Herzensstoß.
Ich gehe durch den Todesschlaf
3775 Zu Gott ein als Soldat und brav.
Stirbt.

NOTES: 3766, 3767, 3769, 3772

22

Dom

Amt, Orgel und Gesang.
Gretchen unter vielem Volke. Böser Geist hinter Gretchen.

BÖSER GEIST
Wie anders, Gretchen, war dir's,
Als du noch voll Unschuld
Hier zum Altar tratst,
Aus dem vergriffnen Büchelchen
3780 Gebete lalltest, —
Halb Kinderspiele,
Halb Gott im Herzen!
Gretchen!
Wo steht dein Kopf?
3785 In deinem Herzen
Welche Missetat?
Bet'st du für deiner Mutter Seele, die
Durch dich zur langen, langen Pein hinüberschlief?
Auf deiner Schwelle wessen Blut? —
3790 Und unter deinem Herzen
Regt sich's nicht quillend schon
Und ängstet dich und sich
Mit ahnungsvoller Gegenwart?

NOTES: Scene 22; 3779, 3786, 3788
60

GRETCHEN
Weh! Weh!
3795 Wär' ich der Gedanken los,
Die mir herüber und hinüber gehen
Wider mich!
CHOR
Dies irae, dies illa
Solvet saeclum in favilla.

Orgelton.
BÖSER GEIST
3800 Grimm faßt dich!
Die Posaune tönt!
Die Gräber beben!
Und dein Herz,
Aus Aschenruh
3805 Zu Flammenqualen
Wieder aufgeschaffen,
Bebt auf!
GRETCHEN
Wär' ich hier weg!
Mir ist, als ob die Orgel mir
3810 Den Atem versetzte,
Gesang mein Herz
Im Tiefsten löste.
CHOR
Judex ergo cum sedebit,
Quidquid latet, adparebit,
3815 *Nil inultum remanebit.*
GRETCHEN
Mir wird so eng!
Die Mauernpfeiler
Befangen mich!
Das Gewölbe
3820 Drängt mich! — Luft!

NOTES: 3795, 3797, 3798, 3800, 3801, 3803, 3811, 3813

BÖSER GEIST

Verbirg dich? Sünd' und Schande [*shame*]
Bleibt nicht verborgen.
— Luft? Licht?
Weh dir!

CHOR

3825 *Quid sum miser tunc dicturus?*
Quem patronum rogaturus,
Cum vix justus sit securus?

BÖSER GEIST

Ihr Antlitz wenden [*Good people turn their faces from you!*]
Verklärte von dir ab.
3830 Die Hände dir zu reichen,
Schauert's den Reinen.
Weh!

CHOR

Quid sum miser tunc dicturus?

GRETCHEN

Nachbarin! Euer Fläschchen!— [*smelling salts*]

Sie fällt in Ohnmacht.

NOTES: 3822, 3825, 3829, 3834

Walpurgisnacht

Mephistopheles has taken Faust off to the revels on the Blocks-berg. Faust participates in the grotesque and indecent celebration. But while he is dancing with a ribald young witch, a red mouse jumps out of her mouth. Faust is understandably shaken by this incident. And then . . .

FAUST

          Mephisto, siehst du dort
Ein blasses, schönes Kind allein und ferne stehen?
4185 Sie schiebt sich langsam nur vom Ort,
Sie scheint mit geschloßnen Füßen zu gehen.
Ich muß bekennen, daß mir deucht,
Daß sie dem guten Gretchen gleicht.

MEPHISTOPHELES

Laß das nur stehn! Dabei wird's niemand wohl.
4190 Es ist ein Zauberbild, ist leblos, ein Idol.
Ihm zu begegnen ist nicht gut:
Vom starren Blick erstarrt des Menschen Blut,
Und er wird fast in Stein verkehrt . . .
Von der Meduse hast du ja gehört!

FAUST

4195 Fürwahr, es sind die Augen eines Toten,
Die eine liebende Hand nicht schloß.

Das ist die Brust, die Gretchen mir geboten,
Das ist der süße Leib, den ich genoß.

MEPHISTOPHELES

Das ist die Zauberei, du leicht verführter Tor!
4200 Denn jedem kommt sie wie sein Liebchen vor.

FAUST

Welch eine Wonne! Welch ein Leiden!
Ich kann von diesem Blick nicht scheiden.
Wie sonderbar muß diesen schönen Hals
Ein einzig rotes Schnürchen schmücken,
4205 Nicht breiter als ein Messerrücken!

MEPHISTOPHELES

Ganz recht! Ich seh' es ebenfalls.
Sie kann das Haupt auch unterm Arme tragen;
Denn Perseus hat's ihr abgeschlagen. —
Nur immer diese Lust zum Wahn! —

... *Mephistopheles takes Faust to a theater on the mountainside, where some dramatic amateurs are putting on a satiric intermezzo, the Walpurgis Night's Dream: Oberon and Titania's Golden Wedding.*

NOTES: 4197, 4207, 4208, 4209

child is born. —
Gu. kills child
← goes begging
Lets put in
jail.
Dark Day

Trüber Tag

Feld.

FAUST. MEPHISTOPHELES.

FAUST Im Elend! Verzweifelnd! Erbärmlich auf der Erde
lange verirrt und nun gefangen! Als Missetäterin im Kerker
zu entsetzlichen Qualen eingesperrt, das holde, unselige
Geschöpf! Bis dahin! dahin! — Verräterischer, nichtswür-
[5] diger Geist, und das hast du mir verheimlicht! — Steh
nur, steh! Wälze die teuflischen Augen ingrimmend im
Kopf herum! Steh und trutze mir durch deine unerträgliche
Gegenwart! — Gefangen! Im unwiederbringlichen Elend!
Bösen Geistern übergeben und der richtenden, gefühl-
[10] losen Menschheit! — Und mich wiegst du indes in abge-
schmackten Zerstreuungen, verbirgst mir ihren wachsenden
Jammer und lässest sie hülflos verderben!

MEPHISTOPHELES Sie ist die erste nicht.

FAUST Hund! Abscheuliches Untier! — Wandle ihn, du
[15] unendlicher Geist! Wandle den Wurm wieder in seine Hundsgestalt, wie er sich oft nächtlicher Weile gefiel, vor mir
herzutrotten, dem harmlosen Wandrer vor die Füße zu
kollern und sich dem niederstürzenden auf die Schultern
zu hängen. Wandl' ihn wieder in seine Lieblingsbildung,
[20] daß er vor mir im Sand auf dem Bauch krieche, ich ihn
mit Füßen trete, den Verworfnen! — „Die erste nicht!"

— Jammer! Jammer! Von keiner Menschenseele zu fassen, daß mehr als ein Geschöpf in die Tiefe dieses Elendes versank, daß nicht das erste genug tat für die Schuld aller [25] übrigen in seiner windenden Todesnot vor den Augen des ewig Verzeihenden! Mir wühlt es Mark und Leben durch, das Elend dieser Einzigen; du grinsest gelassen über das Schicksal von Tausenden hin!

MEPHISTOPHELES Nun sind wir schon wieder an der [30] Grenze unsres Witzes, da, wo euch Menschen der Sinn überschnappt. Warum machst du Gemeinschaft mit uns, wenn du sie nicht durchführen kannst? Willst fliegen, und bist vorm Schwindel nicht sicher? Drangen wir uns dir auf, oder du dich uns?

[35] FAUST Fletsche deine gefräßigen Zähne mir nicht so entgegen! Mir ekelt's! — Großer, herrlicher Geist, der du mir zu erscheinen würdigtest, der du mein Herz kennest und meine Seele, warum an den Schandgesellen mich schmieden, der sich am Schaden weidet und am Verderben [40] sich letzt?

MEPHISTOPHELES Endigst du?

FAUST Rette sie! Oder weh dir! Den gräßlichsten Fluch über dich auf Jahrtausende!

MEPHISTOPHELES Ich kann die Bande des Rächers nicht [45] lösen, seine Riegel nicht öffnen. — „Rette sie!" — Wer war's, der sie ins Verderben stürzte? Ich oder du?

Faust blickt wild umher.

MEPHISTOPHELES Greifst du nach dem Donner? Wohl, daß er euch elenden Sterblichen nicht gegeben ward! Den unschuldig Entgegnenden zu zerschmettern, das ist so [50] Tyrannenart, sich in Verlegenheiten Luft zu machen.

FAUST Bringe mich hin! Sie soll frei sein!

MEPHISTOPHELES Und die Gefahr, der du dich aussetzest? Wisse! Noch liegt auf der Stadt Blutschuld von deiner Hand. Über des Erschlagenen Stätte schweben [55] rächende Geister und lauern auf den wiederkehrenden Mörder.

NOTES: [32, 44, 47, 53, 55]

  FAUST Noch das von dir? Mord und Tod einer Welt
über dich Ungeheuer! Führe mich hin, sag' ich, und befrei
sie.

[60] MEPHISTOPHELES Ich führe dich, und was ich tun kann,
höre! Habe ich alle Macht im Himmel und auf Erden?
Des Türners Sinne will ich umnebeln, bemächtige dich
der Schlüssel und führe sie heraus mit Menschenhand!
Ich wache! Die Zauberpferde sind bereit, ich entführe
[65] euch. Das vermag ich.

  FAUST Auf und davon!

26

Nacht. Offen Feld

*Faust, Mephistopheles, auf schwarzen Pferden daherbrau-
send.*

FAUST
Was weben die dort um den Rabenstein?
MEPHISTOPHELES
4400 Weiß nicht, was sie kochen und schaffen.
FAUST
Schweben auf, schweben ab, neigen sich, beugen sich.
MEPHISTOPHELES
Eine Hexenzunft.
FAUST
Sie streuen und weihen.
MEPHISTOPHELES
Vorbei! Vorbei!

27

[handwritten: This the dar]

Rerker

Faust mit einem Bund Schlüssel und einer Lampe, vor einem eisernen Türchen.

FAUST

4405 Mich faßt ein längst entwohnter Schauer,
Der Menschheit ganzer Jammer faßt mich an.
Hier wohnt sie, hinter dieser feuchten Mauer;
Und ihr Verbrechen war ein guter Wahn! —
Du zauderst, zu ihr zu gehen?
4410 Du fürchtest, sie wiederzusehen?
Fort! Dein Zagen zögert den Tod heran.

Er ergreift das Schloß. Es singt inwendig.

Meine Mutter, die Hur', *[handwritten: whore]*
Die mich umgebracht hat!
Mein Vater, der Schelm, *[handwritten: scoundrel]*
4415 Der mich gessen hat!
Mein Schwesterlein klein
Hub auf die Bein' *[handwritten: picked up bones]*
An einem kühlen Ort.
Da ward ich ein schönes Waldvögelein,
4420 Fliege fort, fliege fort!

FAUST, *aufschließend.*

Sie ahnet nicht, daß der Geliebte lauscht,

NOTES: Scene 27; 4405, 4408, 4411, 4412

60

[handwritten marginal notes: He is afraid to enter lest he should ... ; delay is bad tho.; humanity]

Die Ketten klirren hört, das Stroh, das rauscht.
Er tritt ein.
MARGARETE, *sich auf dem Lager verbergend.*
Weh! weh! Sie kommen! — Bittrer Tod!
FAUST, *leise.*
Still! Still! Ich komme, dich zu befreien.
MARGARETE, *sich vor ihn hinwälzend.*
4425 Bist du ein Mensch, so fühle meine Not!
FAUST
Du wirst die Wächter aus dem Schlafe schreien!
Er faßt die Ketten, sie aufzuschließen.
MARGARETE, *auf den Knien.*
Wer hat dir, Henker, diese Macht
Über mich gegeben?
Du holst mich schon um Mitternacht.
4430 Erbarme dich und laß mich leben!
Ist's morgen früh nicht zeitig genung?
Sie steht auf.
Bin ich doch noch so jung, so jung!
Und soll schon sterben!
Schön war ich auch, und das war mein Verderben.
4435 Nah war der Freund, nun ist er weit;
Zerrissen liegt der Kranz, die Blumen zerstreut . . .
Fasse mich nicht so gewaltsam an!
Schone mich! Was hab' ich dir getan?
Laß mich nicht vergebens flehen,
4440 Hab' ich dich doch mein' Tage nicht gesehen!
FAUST
Werd' ich den Jammer überstehen?
MARGARETE
Ich bin nun ganz in deiner Macht.
Laß mich nur erst das Kind noch tränken.
Ich herzt' es diese ganze Nacht;
4445 Sie nahmen mir's, um mich zu kränken,
Und sagen nun, ich hätt' es umgebracht.

NOTES: 4423, 4436, 4443

Und niemals werd' ich wieder froh. . .
Sie singen Lieder auf mich! Es ist bös von den Leuten!
Ein altes Märchen endigt so;
4450 Wer heißt sie's deuten?

   FAUST *wirft sich nieder.*

Ein Liebender liegt dir zu Füßen,
Die Jammerknechtschaft aufzuschließen.

   MARGARETE *wirft sich zu ihm.*

O laß uns knien, die Heil'gen anzurufen!
Sieh! Unter diesen Stufen,
4455 Unter der Schwelle
Siedet die Hölle!
Der Böse,
Mit furchtbarem Grimme,
Macht ein Getöse! ein

   FAUST, *laut.*

4460 Gretchen! Gretchen!

   MARGARETE, *aufmerksam.*

Das war des Freundes Stimme! nah

  Sie springt auf. Die Ketten fallen ab.

Wo ist er? Ich hab' ihn rufen hören!
Ich bin frei! Mir soll niemand wehren!
An seinen Hals will ich fliegen,
4465 An seinem Busen liegen!
Er rief „Gretchen!" Er stand auf der Schwelle.
Mitten durchs Heulen und Klappen der Hölle,
Durch den grimmigen, teuflischen Hohn,
Erkannt' ich den süßen, den liebenden Ton.

   FAUST

4470 Ich bin's!

   MARGARETE

  Du bist's! O sag es noch einmal!

  Ihn fassend.

Er ist's! Er ist's! Wohin ist alle Qual?
Wohin die Angst des Kerkers, der Ketten?

   NOTES: 4449, 4460.

Du bist's! Kommst, mich zu retten!
Ich bin gerettet!
4475   Schon ist die Straße wieder da,
Auf der ich dich zum ersten Male sah,
Und der heitere Garten,
Wo ich und Marthe deiner warten.

     Faust, *fortstrebend.*

Komm mit! Komm mit!

     Margarete

                O weile!
4480   Weil' ich doch so gern, wo du weilest!

     Liebkosend.

     Faust

Eile!
Wenn du nicht eilest,
Werden wir's teuer büßen müssen.

     Margarete

Wie? Du kannst nicht mehr küssen?
4485   Mein Freund, so kurz von mir entfernt,
Und hast 's Küssen verlernt?
Warum wird mir an deinem Halse so bang,
Wenn sonst von deinen Worten, deinen Blicken
Ein ganzer Himmel mich überdrang,
4490   Und du mich küßtest, als wolltest du mich ersticken?
Küsse mich!
Sonst küss' ich dich!

     Sie umfaßt ihn.

O weh! Deine Lippen sind kalt,
Sind stumm.
4495   Wo ist dein Lieben
Geblieben?
Wer brachte mich drum?

     Sie wendet sich von ihm.

Notes: 4475, 4493

FAUST

Komm! Folge mir! Liebchen, fasse Mut!
Ich herze dich mit tausendfacher Glut;
4500 Nur folge mir! Ich bitte dich nur dies!

MARGARETE, *zu ihm gewendet.*

Und bist du's denn? Und bist du's auch gewiß?

FAUST

Ich bin's! Komm mit!

MARGARETE

               Du machst die Fesseln los,
Nimmst wieder mich in deinen Schoß.
Wie kommt es, daß du dich vor mir nicht scheust? —
4505 Und weißt du denn, mein Freund, wen du befreist?

FAUST

Komm! Komm! Schon weicht die tiefe Nacht.

MARGARETE

Meine Mutter hab' ich umgebracht,
Mein Kind hab' ich ertränkt.
War es nicht dir und mir geschenkt?
4510 Dir auch. — Du bist's! Ich glaub' es kaum.
Gib deine Hand! Es ist kein Traum!
Deine liebe Hand! — Ach, aber sie ist feucht!
Wische sie ab! Wie mich deucht,
Ist Blut dran.
4515 Ach Gott! Was hast du getan!
Stecke den Degen ein;
Ich bitte dich drum!

FAUST

Laß das Vergangne vergangen sein,
Du bringst mich um.

MARGARETE

4520 Nein, du mußt übrigbleiben!
Ich will dir die Gräber beschreiben.
Für die mußt du sorgen
Gleich morgen:
Der Mutter den besten Platz geben,

NOTES: 4512, 4520

4525 Meinen Bruder sogleich darneben,
     Mich ein wenig beiseit',
     Nur nicht gar zu weit!
     Und das Kleine mir an die rechte Brust.
     Niemand wird sonst bei mir liegen! —
4530   Mich an deine Seite zu schmiegen,
     Das war ein süßes, ein holdes Glück!
     Aber es will mir nicht mehr gelingen;
     Mir ist's, als müßt' ich mich zu dir zwingen,
     Als stießest du mich von dir zurück;
4535 Und doch bist du's und blickst so gut, so fromm.
           FAUST
     Fühlst du, daß ich es bin, so komm!
           MARGARETE
     Dahinaus?
           FAUST
     Ins Freie.
                 Ist das Grab drauß,
     Lauert der Tod, so komm!
4540 Von hier ins ewige Ruhebett
     Und weiter keinen Schritt —
     Du gehst nun fort? O Heinrich, könnt' ich mit!
           FAUST
     Du kannst! So wolle nur! Die Tür steht offen.
           MARGARETE
     Ich darf nicht fort; für mich ist nichts zu hoffen.
4545 Was hilft es fliehn? Sie lauern doch mir auf.
     Es ist so elend, betteln zu müssen,
     Und noch dazu mit bösem Gewissen!
     Es ist so elend, in der Fremde schweifen,
     Und sie werden mich doch ergreifen!
           FAUST
4550 Ich bleibe bei dir.

NOTES: 4538, 4545

she means self escaping?

MARGARETE

Geschwind! Geschwind!
Rette dein armes Kind!
Fort! Immer den Weg
Am Bach hinauf,
4555 Über den Steg,
In den Wald hinein,
Links, wo die Planke steht,
Im Teich.
Faß es nur gleich!
4560 Es will sich heben,
Es zappelt noch!
Rette! Rette!

FAUST

Besinne dich doch!
Nur e i n e n Schritt, so bist du frei!

MARGARETE

4565 Wären wir nur den Berg vorbei!
Da sitzt meine Mutter auf einem Stein . . .
— Es faßt mich kalt beim Schopfe! —
Da sitzt meine Mutter auf einem Stein
Und wackelt mit dem Kopfe; *shaking head*
4570 Sie winkt nicht, sie nickt nicht, der Kopf ist ihr schwer,
Sie schlief so lange, sie wacht nicht mehr.
Sie schlief, damit wir uns freuten . . .
Es waren glückliche Zeiten!

FAUST

Hilft hier kein Flehen, hilft kein Sagen,
4575 So wag' ich's, dich hinwegzutragen.

MARGARETE

Laß mich! Nein, ich leide keine Gewalt!
Fasse mich nicht so mörderisch an!
Sonst hab' ich dir ja alles zulieb' getan.

FAUST

Der Tag graut! Liebchen! Liebchen!

NOTES: 4551, 4565, 4567

MARGARETE

4580 Tag! Ja, es wird Tag! Der letzte Tag dringt herein;
Mein Hochzeittag sollt' es sein! —
Sag niemand, daß du schon bei Gretchen warst.
Weh meinem Kranze!
Es ist eben geschehn!
4585 Wir werden uns wiedersehn;
Aber nicht beim Tanze. —
Die Menge drängt sich, man hört sie nicht.
Der Platz, die Gassen
Können sie nicht fassen.
4590 Die Glocke ruft, das Stäbchen bricht.
Wie sie mich binden und packen!
Zum Blutstuhl bin ich schon entrückt.
Schon zuckt nach jedem Nacken
Die Schärfe, die nach meinem zückt . . .
4595 Stumm liegt die Welt wie das Grab!

FAUST

O, wär' ich nie geboren!

MEPHISTOPHELES *erscheint draußen.*

Auf! Oder ihr seid verloren!
Unnützes Zagen! Zaudern und Plaudern!
Meine Pferde schaudern,
4600 Der Morgen dämmert auf.

MARGARETE

Was steigt aus dem Boden herauf?
Der! Der! Schick ihn fort!
Was will der an dem heiligen Ort?
Er will mich!

FAUST

Du sollst leben!

MARGARETE

4605 Gericht Gottes! Dir hab' ich mich übergeben!

MEPHISTOPHELES, *zu Faust.*

Komm! Komm! Ich lasse dich mit ihr im Stich!

NOTES: 4583, 4590, 4593, 4595, 4599, 4603, 4606

MARGARETE

Dein bin ich, Vater! Rette mich! —
Ihr Engel! Ihr heiligen Scharen!
Lagert euch umher, mich zu bewahren! —
4610 Heinrich! Mir graut's vor dir!

MEPHISTOPHELES

Sie ist gerichtet! ~~INDEED~~

STIMME *von oben.*

Ist gerettet! ~~SAVED~~

MEPHISTOPHELES, *zu Faust.*

Her zu mir!

Verschwindet mit Faust.

STIMME, *von innen, verhallend.*

Heinrich! — Heinrich! — —

NOTES: 4609, 4610, 4611, 4612

Faust

PART TWO

Faust recovers from his exhaustion and remorse at Gretchen's fate. He and Mephistopheles achieve high political influence by making themselves indispensable to the emperor. They solve his financial problems by an inflationary issuance of unsecured paper money. They entertain him with elaborate masquerade spectacles. Faust even conjures up the spirits of Paris and Helen of Troy. He becomes infatuated with Helen and dedicates himself to the quest for this epitome of beauty.

An elaborate procedure (Act II of the Second Part) prepares for the meeting of Faust and Helen. There is a Classical Walpurgisnacht in which many figures of classical legend appear and prepare the way for Faust's esthetic conquest of beauty.

In the third act, Faust meets and wins Helen of Troy. The moment of supreme esthetic achievement is incomplete and necessarily transitory. Euphorion, the son of Faust and Helen, has inherited his father's boundless ambition. Attempting to fly, he leaps to his death; and Helen departs to the underworld to be with him.

Act IV introduces a new field of endeavor: a socially constructive urge to power and control. Faust plans to reclaim shore land from the sea. To secure legal authority and practical implementation for this project, he (with Mephistopheles' help) wins a victory for the emperor over a threatening faction of rebels. The emperor grants Faust a fief over the shore regions.

In the final act, Faust is a very old man. He has almost completed the reclamation project. He is the monarch of his newly-created province; his ships carry commerce to and from all parts of the world, and bring the world's wealth to Faust's palace. But Faust is still not completely satisfied. He wants a neighboring farm, up on the dunes. Its owners (Philemon and Baucis) are killed by Faust's ruffianly employees when he orders a forcible removal to a new farm in the reclaimed land. Also, Faust finds it necessary to drain a swamp, to assure the health of his future community. He thinks of that community: free, but never free from danger; for the sea outside will demand constant vigilance, energy, fore-sighted cooperation of all citizens against the ever-present peril. The anticipation of these future fruits of his planning brings him the highest moment of his life. Faust falls dead, as Mephistopheles claims victory. But the soul of Faust is snatched from Mephistopheles by a chorus of angels, who chant: 'He who uses his energy in ever striving onward — him we can save!'

Faust is first assigned to the company of stillborn children. But almost at once he has outgrown them. His future evolution is entrusted to one of the blessed penitents, who was formerly known by the name of Gretchen.

Notes

The scenes from FAUST which portray the tragedy of
the deserted sweetheart, Gretchen, do not stem from
the traditional Faust story. They embody rather the
revolt of eighteenth century individualism against the
pedantically harsh treatment of the unfortunate victims
of nature's strongest impulse. The catastrophe of the
deserted Gretchen is the inevitable resolution of this
conflict between nature and a human society which
does not dare to permit the free sway of impulses and
which has to exact expiation for the transgression of its
laws, whether this transgression result from crass lewd-
ness or from yielding to the impulses of the purest love.

The desertion of the sweetheart, rather than the
socially acceptable justification through wedlock, is the
result of a second strong natural impulse, the drive for
individual freedom. To a man of any human dignity
this act of desertion brings the feeling of guilt and the
need to perform expiation. Part I of Goethe's FAUST
concludes with the tragedy of Gretchen. The Gretchen
episode is a part only of the total problem of Faust, and
the final resolution of the problem involves more than
guilt and expiation on this score alone.

9. Straße

2605 **Fräulein** This form of address in Goethe's day was proper
only to persons of the nobility. Commoners were addressed
as *Jungfrau* (3018) or *Jungfer*.

2606 **Ihr** dative of *Sie*, used like *Er* as a pronoun of address.
Three pronouns could be used to address one person: the
most intimate, *du;* next in degree of formality, *Er* or *Sie*
(with a third person singular verb); most formal, *Ihr* (with a
second person plural verb).

2607–8 The rime **schön : gehn** here (and 3055:3058), while impure in the strict sense of the word, was permissible in Goethe's day and came naturally to him since he unrounded the vowels *ü, ö* and the diphthong *eu, äu* in his usual speech. Hence we find such rimes as *könnte : Sakramente* 3422:3423, or *betrüben: lieben* 2869:2870, or *müssen : zerrissen* 3036:3038, or *Freuden: weiden* 2670:2671, *deucht : gleicht* 4187:4188, *weit : zerstreut* 4435:4436. Goethe also spoke final *–g* as a spirant (*ch*); hence such rimes as *lag : nach* 3128:3129.

2619 **Dirne** Originally without pejorative connotation, this word even before Goethe's day had fallen from good usage except when applied to girls from the country, *Bauerndirnen*. The Romantic poets tried to reinstate this old word in its earlier pleasant flavor. Nevertheless, this line sounds a bit coarse and brutal, and line 2627 is indubitably so.

2624 **unschuldig** = *unschuldiges*. In poetry, the attributive adjective after an *ein*-word in the nominative or accusative neuter singular is quite frequently without the expected ending *–es*.

2627 **Jahr** the uninflected form after a numeral instead of the plural form *Jahre*, which is now required. Goethe uses both forms.

2628 **Hans Liederlich** Jack the Dissolute. Such forms are frequent in German: *Hans Nimmersatt, Hans Ohnesorge, Hans-im-Gluck.*

2630 **dünkelt ihm** The subject is an impersonal *es:* 'in his conceit he imagines...'

2633 **Magister Lobesan** a name formed like *Hans Liederlich*. The connotation is that of a dogmatic academician, who lays down the law to his listeners.

2634 **Gesetz** Faust understands line 2632 to concern the legal impediment to the fulfillment of his desires. Mephistopheles has merely indicated that some things are beyond his powers to procure (2626), and indeed that some things may even be impossible for Faust.

2639 **mag** is here used in its older meaning of 'can'; **gehn und stehn** is a fixed, riming phrase which means 'be done.'

2645 **Franzos** The French novel of amatory adventure led to the use of *ein Franzos* as a symbol for a roué or rake.

2651 **geknetet** Supply *habt*. The auxiliary of tense is often omitted in this way, particularly in subordinate clauses.

2652 **welsche Geschicht'** refers to the notably lubricious and lascivious renaissance love romances from Italy or from France, for example, the Italian Boccaccio (1313–1375) or the French Margaret of Navarre (1492–1549).

2654 **Schimpf** here in its older meaning of 'jest,' hence a synonym for **Spaß**.

2674 Mephistopheles' use of the foreign words *reüssieren* and *revidieren* contributes to the impression of sophistication and lubricity he makes here and contrasts with the hot impetuosity of the newly enamored Faust.

2675 Buried treasure is generally thought to be in the devil's care.

10. *Abend*

The function of this scene is to make vivid the basic contrast and hence the conflict between Margarete's simple purity of heart and the foul baseness of the threat to her peace. Neither Faust's passion nor Mephistopheles' lewd sensuality is compatible with the cleanliness of this room and its occupant.

The atmosphere of the room has its effect upon Faust. His passion is, for the moment, sublimated in a romantic analysis of the objects around him, until he finally realizes the incongruity of his present undertaking with his former standards of conduct (2720). Mephistopheles intervenes before this turn of thought can become effective in action which might disrupt his plans.

2683 **keck** namely, in lines 2605–2606.

2688 **Der du** The style is reminiscent of the Lord's Prayer: "*Vater unser, der du bist im Himmel . . .*"

2694 **Kerker** a clear indication that this lover would regard permanent residence here as imprisonment.

2696 **empfangen** Supply *hast*.

2706 After the floor has been duly scrubbed, sand is strewn upon it, and fastidious housewives arrange the sand in ornamental patterns, or at any rate, in undulating lines.

2708 **Hütte** Throughout his works Goethe employs the *Hütte* as a symbol of peace, happiness, and contentment — an ideal

state of life, which often becomes the target of the destructive
impulses of self-assertion, self-expression, and desire for power.

2711 With **bildetest** supply a subject *du.*

2712 The angelic quality of this girl is innate; after her birth
nature has merely developed it. The process is restated in
lines 2715–2716.

2714 **den Busen** an accusative absolute.

2715 **Weben** The 'weaving' is probably best understood in the
sense of Luther's translation of Genesis 1.21: "*Gott schuf
allerlei Tier, das da lebt und webt.*" Hence the noun *Weben*
means 'the free movement of a living being.'

2720 Faust recognizes the despicable intention which brought him
here. A conflict seems about to arise within him. But his
senses and his lust are too strong, though some change has
come over him. The forthright urge to animal indulgence
has changed, with the dissolution of his emotions, into a dream
of love.

2732 **woanders** He has 'found' it, never mind where.

2736 **eine andere** Mephistopheles says he put jewels into this box
to enable Faust to win a different sort of lady. The contents
of the casket will assuredly astonish so simple and ingenuous
a girl as this Gretchen.

2737 The game is the same and the person involved is not important.

2738 **soll ich?** The hesitancy is in the face of the decision to seduce
or not to seduce this maiden.

2739 Mephistopheles, as is frequently the case, fails to understand
Faust's motive for hesitation and thinks in terms of his own
patterns of behavior.

2740 **Eurer Lüsternheit** 'Your Greediness,' a title like 'Your High-
ness.'

2744 Gestures of extreme exertion, mental and physical.

2751 The subjects of the lecture he seems about to deliver.

2753 The sinister intruders have left an ominous, oppressive atmosphere behind them.

2758 **töricht-furchtsam** = *töricht-furchtsames.* See note to line
2624.

2759 A ballad which has often been set to music, notably by Liszt,
Schumann, Gounod, and Berlioz. The melody most frequently heard, however, is that by Zelter (1821). — It is a
song about the faithful lover, which the workings of Margarete's subconscious mind have brought to focus.

2761 **Buhle** The emotional value of this word is usually unpleasant
or pejorative, either mildly, as in the case of a paramour, or
more violently, when used of persons on a lower social level.

2775 **Zecher** The king is so called, because he is at the moment
drinking at a gay banquet. It is not necessary to believe that
he was on that account a habitual heavy drinker.

2781 **täten ... sinken** This use of the auxiliary past-tense form
of *tät* or *täten* with an infinitive in place of a simple past-tense
form is a characteristic feature of the style of the folk-song.

2786–2787 These lines indicate that Margarete's family was mod-
erately well-to-do, so that upon occasion the mother could
lend money to persons who needed ready cash. It is not likely
that Goethe thought of the mother as a professional pawn-
broker.

2800 'But people pay no attention to those qualities.' Beauty and
youth are not enough; one must be really wealthy in order
to attract a fine suitor.

11. Spaziergang

This *Spaziergang* is a 'Promenade,' a place suitable for strolling,
perhaps outside the city, perhaps on its walls.

The function of the scene is three-fold. It retards the progress of
the main action of the Gretchen adventure, it introduces Gretchen's
mother as an opposing force in that conflict, and it removes the last
uncertainty as to Faust's scruples (2730, 2738), or his determination to have this girl (2857).

2805 **Elemente** A very frequent, rather strong oath, the origin of
which is not known. It may be pointed out that it rimes with
Sakrament and may be a substitute for this word, but this is
not demonstrable. If it is one of the four elements, it is
probably fire.

2807 **Was hast?** 'What's the matter? What ails you?'

2808 **So kein Gesicht sah ich** that is, *So ein Gesicht sah ich nie.*

2812 Irony.

2814 **Pfaff** has a strongly pejorative connotation of contempt and disgust.

2817 **gar einen feinen** that is, *einen gar feinen.*

2823–2824 **ungerechtes Gut** reflects Proverbs 10.2 "*Unrecht Gut hilft nicht,*" or as the popular version has it: "*Unrecht Gut gedeiht nicht.*"

2828 **geschenkter Gaul** The proverb says: "*Einem geschenkten Gaul sieht man nicht ins Maul.*"

2830 **gebracht** Supply *hat.*

2835 Reflects several verses of the second chapter of Revelation, which promise various rewards 'to him that overcometh,' (Verses 7, 11, 17 and 26), or to chapter 21.7: 'He that overcometh shall inherit these things.'

2838 **übergessen** The participle of the inseparable compound *überessen,* arrived at by dropping the *ge-* from *gegessen.* The form *gessen* was historically the original past participle of *essen,* and as such is regularly used in the sixteenth and early seventeenth centuries. People who know this sometimes make a participle without the *-g-,* and say: *sie hatten sich überessen,* but *übergessen* is more frequent.

2843 The subject of **strich … ein** is the priest.

2849 **Gretchen** Faust always uses this form of the girl's name. Goethe writes her name in the stage directions *Margarete* in the scenes with lyric or elegiac quality and *Gretchen* in the scenes with tragic tone, except in the final scene, where *Margarete* is used, and at line 3006, where *Gretchen* occurs.

2851 Faust brought her the jewels, and Gretchen thinks of Faust. Whether or not she suspects him of bringing them is of less consequence, but she could hardly fail to make the connection.

2852 **gebracht** Supply *hat.*

2854 **neu** = *neues.* See note to line 2624.

2857 mach! 'Do something!'

2859 Teufel has been construed as an expletive, a vocative, or as a predicate nominative. **Brei** is thick porridge, which flows sluggishly, like molasses in January. Hence either: 'Confound it, don't be slow about it!' or 'You devil, don't be slow about it!' or 'Be a devil, but just don't be slow about this!'

2861 Faust has asserted his authority with some vehemence and Mephistopheles replies, as a servant would reply, with *'gnädiger Herr.'* If there is irony in his voice it is not sufficient to stop Faust in his departure.

2863 Euch instead of *einem* (dative of *man*) includes the audience in the group of those who are being imposed upon by this extravagant lover.

12. Der Nachbarin Haus

The function of this scene is to prepare for the tryst between Faust and Margarete. It is difficult to imagine how Mephistopheles could have arranged a more favorable site for the love-affair he is to promote than he finds ready-made in the house and garden of Gretchen's older friend, Marthe.

2868 auf dem Stroh Probably an allusion to *Strohwitwe*, a woman whose husband has been away from home for a long time.

2869 tät... betrüben equivalent to *betrübte;* see note to line 2781.

2872 The death certificate would make it possible for Marthe to take another husband.

2873 Gretelchen a double diminutive, with somewhat saccharine connotation.

2879 Sie See note to line 2606.

2880 Tät serves equally well as subjunctive past in these auxiliary forms: **tät's tragen** 'would carry.'

2883 Gassen an old dative singular form.

2884 mit instead of *damit.*

2889 gibt's 'there will be.'

2896 Vorhängel Most old European houses had some kind of arrangement which permitted those inside to see who was at the door before they unlocked it. In this case (as in Storm's *Immensee*) it is a peep-window with a curtain.

2897 **Bin so frei** The standard reply in accepting a favor offered by a superior, here the request to enter.

2902 Mephistopheles pretends to think Margarete a fine lady, because he finds her adorned with a precious necklace and pearl earrings.

2903 **genommen** Supply *habe*.

2906 See note to line 2605 concerning *Fräulein*.

2911 The use of **Sie hat** and **bringt Er** (2913) as second person forms is formal or 'polite' speech for these people. See note to line 2606.

2921–2922 Tragic irony: this is precisely what happens to her.

2923 Mephistopheles is not wholly conventional here. The first half of his statement is nearly universal. Proverbs 14.13: 'Even in laughter the heart is sorrowful and the end of mirth is heaviness,' or Chaucer, in the Nun's Priest's Tale (line 4395): 'For evere the latter ende of joye is wo.' What is unusual is the second half of the sentence. He evidently knows that Marthe is not one long to pine over the death of a husband, and certainly constancy in Marthe would fit poorly with Mephistopheles' schemes.

2926 The basilica of St. Anthony in Padua is one of the finest structures of its kind. The tomb of the Saint is in a splendidly decorated chapel in the basilica, a quite incongruous resting place for the remains of the errant Schwerdtlein.

2927–2928 *an einer Stätte wohlgeweiht zum ewig kühlen Ruhebette* would be the more usual order.

2931 According to the old custom, masses for the dead were said at the funeral service, and on the third, seventh, and thirtieth days after a person's death, and on the anniversaries of his passing.

2943 This brief but important exchange with Margarete is managed while Marthe turns away to quiet her weeping.

2946 **Galan** a high-sounding foreign word (from Spain) for the native *Buhle*.

2948 The **lieb Ding** is the *Galan*, whom Mephistopheles is recom-
mending to Margarete.

2954 **hätte**   The subjunctive softens the assertion of Schwerdtlein's
turpitude and gives it a cautious and polite tone.

2968 **aller Treu', aller Lieb'** genitives, objects of *vergessen*, now
regularly with the accusative, as in line 3333.

2970 **Euch** the so-called ethical dative, indicating the person according to whose desire something is done.

2974 Naval warfare between Turkish and Christian merchant
ships was incessant well down into the eighteenth century.
Each party plundered the ships of the other whenever it
could do so.

2981 **Ein schönes Fräulein** is euphemistic for a street-walker.   The
form of the word **Napel**, for *Neapel*, suggests the *mal de
Naples*, syphilis, which is probably the lasting gift the lady
gave Mr. Schwerdtlein.

2992 **mein erster** hints that she is ready to entertain the idea of
finding *einen zweiten*.

2998 Marriage with Schwerdtlein was a possible arrangement,
provided he overlooked about the same amount and kind of
transgression on the lady's part.

3000 **nachgesehen**   Supply *hat*.

3005 **Wort** the promise of 3001–3002.

3007 This aside is an astonishing lapse from the cynicism characteristic of Mephistopheles.   It serves to create very strong
sympathy for Gretchen in the audience, since her fate moves
even the Devil to compassion.

3009 **Zeugnis**   Marthe wishes some legally valid evidence that her
husband is dead, so that she can publish the fact of his death
in the local paper, thereby making her status as a widow
legally clear.   In the absence of a proper death certificate the
facts can be established by the testimony of witnesses in
court (3016).

3010 Supply *ist*.

3013 The theory was that if two witnesses testified to the same
effect their testimony must be true.

3020 **Fräuleins** a plural in –*s* like *Mädels, Jungens;* here the indirect object of *erweist*.

3024 **der Herrn** a genitive plural, predicate to *warten*.

13. Straße

This little scene exhibits the state of Faust's emotions, and furnishes motivation for the scene which follows.

3030 **Kuppler- und Zigeunerwesen** are coupled in this phrase, probably because gypsy women practiced the arts of clairvoyance and divination to predict the future of the love affairs of the young people of the community. From this it is a short step to the business of a procurer.

3031 **was** for *etwas*.

3037 **Sancta Simplicitas** Latin, 'Holy Innocence!' an exclamation said to have been uttered by John Hus, when he saw an old woman throw a fagot into the fire to feed the flames by which he was being burned to death (1415 in Constance).

3040 **Da wärt Ihr's nun!** 'There you are!' or 'Isn't that just like you!'

3050 **Sophiste** The essence of sophistry is the fallaciousness of the sophist's reasoning. The fallacy here is the argument (secundum quid) from the proposition 'Faust as professor of theology has stated as true many things which he did not know to be true' to the conclusion 'Faust could with equal propriety testify falsely concerning Schwerdtlein's death.'

3051 That is, 'Yes, you might call me a liar and a sophist with some justification, if I did not know that very soon you yourself would be just as much a liar and a sophist in your relationship with this girl.'

3057 The incomplete sentence implies the idea: *wird die Rede sein,* 'there will be talk (about eternal fidelity...).'

3072 This line concedes that Faust means to deceive and betray Gretchen, and it gives as his reason for this action his inability to do otherwise because of the compelling force of his impulses. — It is the poet's task to make this appear credible.

14. Garten

This scene and the next display the first tryst between the two lovers. The chief function of the scenes is to demonstrate the purity of the girl and the genuineness of her love for Faust. The contrasts between Gretchen and Marthe and between Faust and Mephistopheles, as the pairs pass alternately before us, are used to emphasize the differences between nature at work and the devil, or if you prefer, society, at play.

When the scene opens, the visit of Faust and Mephistopheles is well along in its course. We have been spared the sight of Faust's perjury concerning Marthe's husband. Also the rather difficult business of Gretchen's first meeting with the dashing galant, who has twice sent her jewels with obvious intent, is skipped; and the pair has reached a comfortable stage in their conversation when we first see them.

3081 **Inkommodiert** A distinguished foreign word to fit a distinguished guest from a different social level.

3091 **kömmt** The only occurrence in FAUST of this archaic form of the third person singular present indicative of *kommen.*

3094 **weiten** an archaic adverbial form.

3112 **spat** an old adverbial form beside *spät*, used in FAUST only in conjunction with *früh*, or for the sake of a rime.

3118 **vor der Stadt** 'just outside the city.' In the older towns with walls the burghers had their gardens outside the limits of these fortifications.

3122 **liebe** like English 'blessed,' is used at times to indicate a mildly unpleasant connotation.

3146 **wie heut so morgen** 'tomorrow the same as today.'

3147 'Under these circumstances one isn't always fresh and lively, full of courage.'

3153 **nichts** is equivalent to *niemand.*

3155–3156 The proverb says: "*Eigner Herd ist Goldes wert,*" and the virtuous wife is praised in Proverbs 31.10: "*Wem ein tugendsam Weib beschert ist, die ist viel edler denn die köstlichsten Perlen.*" 'To the man who has one, a virtuous wife is more precious than the choicest pearls.' — The Devil is citing Scripture for his purpose, which at the moment is evasion.

3174 **Dirne** The word is chosen to reflect what Gretchen thought Faust thought she was, at their first encounter.

3176 **hier** in her heart.— **begonnte** is an old weak past-tense form of *beginnen*, regularly used by Goethe in his youth but not in the second part of FAUST.

3179 **Was soll das?** 'What is that meant to be?' and the answer: "*Es soll nur ein Spiel.*" 'Only a game is intended. I'm just going to play a little game.' The game is the *Liebesorakel* of 3181–3183.

3198 **niemand nichts** Double negation is frequent in natural, colloquial speech, but has been frowned upon in careful prose since someone put forward the heresy that two negatives make an affirmative. Goethe used these double negative forms at times in his most dignified prose. They often give added emphasis or intensity to the utterance.

3204 **der Lauf der Welt** alludes to the second chapter of Ephesians, which deals with the evils of unredeemed life with its governing lusts of the flesh and anger prior to the coming of Christ. The meaning here is simple: 'That is the way things go in this (wicked) world.'

15. Ein Gartenhäuschen

The scene is the interior of the summer house in the garden. The action is so brief that it is commonly staged as part of the preceding scene.

3213–3216 There is nothing in the existing garden scene which would justify the words of Margarete, for up to this point Faust has said almost nothing, while listening to a great deal.

16. Wald und Höhle

The principal raison d'être for this scene is its presentation of Faust as a man of high intelligence caught in a great emotional struggle. Taken with the next scene, *Gretchens Stube*, it constitutes a symmetrical structure by giving two soul-revealing scenes of self-examination, one devoted to Faust and the other to Gretchen, which might be thought of as occurring simultaneously rather than one after the other, as the exigencies of the theater dictate.

We have to picture Faust in a forest glade, to which he has withdrawn to think. The landscape is not gloomy, but is wild, rocky, mountainous, and, for a lazy fellow like Mephistopheles, arduous and dank. There is a grotto into which Faust could withdraw and before which he stands.

In the dialogue which follows, Mephistopheles brings all his cunning to bear upon the problem of getting Faust out of the woods and back to his amorous adventure with Gretchen, which has not yet reached its culmination. He first reproaches Faust for what he thinks is a return to morbid, solitary communion with nature. This course once led Faust to the brink of suicide and will again exhaust and ruin him, if he persists in it. Then Mephistopheles ridicules the incongruity between this great intellectual ambition (as he conceives Faust to feel it) and Faust's overpowering sexual drive, which has been aroused in the Witch's Kitchen and by Gretchen. And then Mephistopheles turns to sheer sensuous incitement, until Faust has been whipped to a frenzy of emotion.

3251 **Leben**   This 'life' is the solitude of *Wald und Höhle* which Mephistopheles finds intolerable.

3254 **Neuen** a weak form instead of the usual strong form *Neuem*, chosen here for the sake of the rime.

3256 The implication is that Faust also has his bad days, when he is much less at peace with himself than in the present scene.

3258 **darfst . . . nicht** 'you have no grounds for . . .'

3268 **Kribskrabs der Imagination** is a reference to the state of mind in which Mephistopheles first found Faust. Faust was a scholar and a university professor who was overcome by frustration and confusion in his search for truth. To Mephistopheles this was 'nonsense' and he had indeed induced Faust to turn his back upon that life *auf Zeiten lang* 'for quite some time.' Now he finds Faust in this wilderness and believes that this behavior threatens a return to the state of confusion and frustration in which he first found Faust, despairing, and on the brink of suicide.

3274–3275 Faust has apparently been drinking from springs and small streams and eating water cress and similar delicacies. This is abhorrent to Mephistopheles, who implies that only toads, very despicable beasties, do this. He can imagine a Ph.D. doing something of this kind, but not a proper human being. The reason for this antipathy of Mephistopheles to Faust's communion with nature becomes clear from a letter which Goethe wrote to Herder, August 9, 1776: *"Ich führe mein Leben in Klüften, Höhlen, Wäldern, in Teichen, unter*

> *Wässerfällen, bei den Unterirdischen, und weide mich aus in Gottes Welt.*" This also illuminates lines 3278–3281, for such retirement into nature was a normal procedure for our poet.

3283–3292   The drastic erotic imagery of this speech serves Mephistopheles' purposes in two ways: It satirizes Faust's delight in pure intellectual speculation; and it prepares for more overt appeals to Faust's passion.

3287   The allusion is to the first chapter of Genesis, which tells of God's work of creation.

3291–3292   'And then to bring this lofty intuitive "insight" to a close — I dare not say how.' The gesture called for by the stage direction presumably indicates copulation.

3293   Mephistopheles: 'You find that hard to take.'

3294   Bitterly ironical.

3298   **vorzulügen**   The allusion is to Faust's conviction that he can intuitively or rationally know everything and penetrate the central secrets of the universe. The **Vergnügen** of line 3297 is the same as that of line 3282.

3300   **abgetrieben**   'worn out' by the days in the forest, as Mephistopheles thinks of them. — According to another interpretation, *abgetrieben* is used in the nautical sense: 'drifted off course.' — The shift in the pronouns of address reflects a shift in attitude from distant politeness (*Euch, Ihr*) to irritated contempt (*Ihm, Er*) to cajoling intimacy (*du*).

3303   **dadrinne** = *dadrinnen* accompanied by a gesture pointing toward the town: 'In yonder!'

3307–3310   The metaphor is that of a spring torrent in a mountain brook. Faust's wooing is compared with the torrent of a mountain stream swollen with melted snow. Such torrents last but a short while, after which the brook becomes a shallow stream.

3318   A well-known folksong begins:

> "Wenn ich ein Vöglein wär'
> Und auch zwei Flügel hätt',
> Flög' ich zu dir..."

3324   **Schlange**   The serpent, according to Genesis 3, was the first and a very successful tempter of the first human beings.

3325 'I'll wager that I capture you!' This remark indicates Mephistopheles' satisfaction with the effect of his suggestions upon
his intended victim. Since the words are spoken to no one
in particular, the expression: 'I'll wager' (*Gelt*) is not a
proposal, but an expression of confidence.

3326 **Hebe dich** ... The phrase is reminiscent of Christ's words to
the devil, Matthew 4.10, which Luther rendered: "*Heb dich
weg von mir, Satan!*" — There is an analogy between the
temptation of Christ in the wilderness and Mephistopheles'
incitement of Faust in this scene.

3329 **halbverrückte Sinnen** Having once put his desire away, Faust
protests against its being brought again to his senses, distraught by the conflict between his conscience and his lust.

3334 The 'Body of the Lord' is either the image of Christ on the
Crucifix, as Gretchen kisses it, or the Bread of the Holy
Sacrament.

3335 **indes** that is, while Faust is not with her.

3337 **Zwillingspaar** A direct allusion to the Song of Songs 4.5,
which Luther rendered: "*Deine zwei Brüste sind wie zwei
junge Rehzwillinge, die unter den Rosen weiden.*"

3339 **Bub'** for *Buben*. This kind of contraction in pairs of words
joined by *und* is frequently met in FAUST. Both words here
are general in meaning: 'male and female.'

3340–3341 A scurrilous interpretation of Genesis 1.27–28: 'And
God created man in his own image, in the image of God
created he him: male and female created he them. And God
blessed them: and God said to them, Be fruitful, and multi-
ply, and replenish the earth, and subdue it ...' — **Beruf**
alludes to *Kuppler* (3338). Faust has called Mephistopheles
a pander and Mephistopheles maintains that God recog-
nized this as the noblest calling and practiced it Himself by
bringing Adam and Eve together.

3349 **Unmensch** 'brute,' by contrast to the composed and purpose-
ful *Mensch*, or 'human being,' he ought to be. These lines
(3350–3360) symbolize the ruin brought about by irresistible
natural forces.

3352 **mit kindlich dumpfen Sinnen** 'childlike, with senses half-
aroused.'

3369 **er** is the man with *das Köpfchen*, or, *der Kopf*, which is implied in *das Köpfchen*.

3372–3373 Since a devil has nothing for which to hope, despair on his part is a silly waste of time and a complete lack of realism.

17. Gretchens Stube

Gretchen's distress is not at all based on the belief that Faust has deserted her (3330–3331), though lines 3315–3319 fit her condition well enough. She is in love and this alone robs her of her peace.

The scene is a necessary antecedent and motivation to the discussion of religion in Marthe's garden, and without this scene *Am Spinnrade* we could not understand Gretchen's acceptance of the sleeping potion for her mother (3514–3515).

Despite the fact that this monologue has frequently been set to music and is indeed an inseparable fusion of lyric and dramatic mood, the words are not a song, like *der König in Thule* (2759–2782), but a soliloquy. The composition of these lines by Schubert is an incomparable gem, the perfect union of great poetry with great music.

Gretchen am Spinnrade The women of Goethe's day, both of peasant and of small town circles, were likely to spend any leisure moments they could find at their spinning wheels.

3378 **Wo** 'Any place in which he is not with me.'

3392 A reference to repeated trysts in her neighbor's garden, such as the one in the scenes *Garten* and *Gartenhäuschen* 3073–3216, and the one to come, 3414–3520.

18. Marthens Garten

Having shown us the emotional state of the two young people, the poet brings them together in the garden. Again as in the first Garden Scene (3073–3204) we are plunged into the middle of a conversation during one of a number of such meetings between the lovers in this convenient trysting spot.

The function of this scene is to exhibit the conquest of Gretchen by Faust (3505–3520) and to provide the motivation which makes tragedy inescapable in this case (3511).

3414 **Heinrich** The Faust of the legend before Goethe was *Johann*. In order to exclude the vulgar associations connected with the name *Johann Faustus*, particularly in the puppet plays,

Goethe selected a different given name. The reasons for his choice of the name *Heinrich* are not certainly known.

3415 'Just how *do* you feel about religion?'

3422 **auf dich könnte** = *über dich vermöchte* 'O, if only I had any influence upon you!'

3428 **magst...fragen** 'Ask, if you wish...'

3429–3430 **Spott über den Frager** because the answer of theologians and philosophers is in terms of names (3457), which mock the real seeker after truth and conceal the true divinity rather than reveal it.

3432 The declaration of faith which Faust here gives is usually viewed as the most eloquent expression of Goethe's pantheistic belief in God. In so far as the utterance is pantheistic it is most like the philosophy of Spinoza. In the main, however, it is the expression on the one hand of the impatience of the men of the Storm and Stress with the inadequacy of mere names, and on the other of the intuitive belief in love as the central principle of the universe.

3447 'Does not the divinity, all these things, you and I, the sky above, and the earth below, life, in short, — crowd in upon your senses and your feelings, forever mysteriously visible in the invisible close beside you?'

3451 **so groß es ist** 'to its full capacity.'

3456–3458 Feeling is the all-important thing; a name is noise and smoke, which beclouds the glowing light of heaven. In sum, the mere confession: *Ich glaube an Gott*, may well enough be completely empty; but the person whose heart is completely full of God's all-pervasive spirit cannot help but confess his faith in that spirit.

3460 The priest tells her too that God is a mysterious presence and that he is present in all things, that God is love, and that one must love God.

3463 **unter dem himmlischen Tage** 'wherever the light of Heaven shines.'

3470 **der** has demonstrative force, 'in that company.'

3475 **widrig** perhaps rather in the sense of 'hostile' than 'repulsive.'

3480 **dem** demonstrative, 'that.'

3488 The double negative gives added emphasis. See note to line 3198.

3490 **mag** = *vermag* 'he is (not) able.'

3492 **hingegeben warm** 'warm in my surrender.'

3494 Faust recognizes and appreciates this girl's intuitive perception of evil.

3496 **wo ... nur** 'where ever.'

3498 'I couldn't pray at all,' no matter how much she might wish to do so.

3501 'This is just a case of natural antipathy,' the opposite of a natural affinity.

3505 In order to understand the character of this girl, it is necessary to understand the customs of her country and her day. It was not at all unusual for a respectable girl to admit her suitor to her bed before wedlock. Gretchen's fault is that she, with her *kindlich dumpfen Sinnen*, fails clearly to distinguish between a lover and a suitor, although she is at times aware of the reality of the case, and she knows that her mother would not regard Faust as a proper person to be her companion. Church and society placed severe penalties on young women who were deserted by their lovers. An example is the scene *Am Brunnen*, 3544–3586.

3511 One may assume that this situation has been foreseen by Faust (see 3209), and that he has asked Mephistopheles what to do. Mephistopheles has given him a sleeping potion which he in turn gives to Gretchen. Gretchen's mother ultimately dies from taking this sleeping draught. Some see in this merely the result of Gretchen's anxiety and fear of being apprehended by her mother, a fear which led her to give her mother an over-dose of the potion. Others see in this the evil treachery of Mephistopheles, who gives Faust a slow-working, deadly poison in the guise of a harmless sleeping draught and thereby places the onus of murder on Faust if Gretchen's mother dies. A similar act of treachery toward Faust is the act of Mephistopheles in destroying Philemon and Baucis in Part II.

3512 **In ihren Trank** Supply *gegossen*.

3523 **wurden** the so-called plural of majesty, used in particularly
      formal speech to lofty personages; hence *Ihnen* in the next
      line.

3527 Girls, says Mephistopheles, believe that wholly orthodox re-
      ligious belief on the part of a husband-to-be is a good omen
      for their future ability to control the man of the house.

3531–3532 'Which in her sight is absolutely the only way to sal-
      vation.'

3534 **übersinnlicher sinnlicher** a trope (oxymoron) which brings
      together two alternating attributes: at one time this suitor
      is above all sensuous motives, at another he is all amorous
      desire. In sum, he is befuddled.

3536 Plato said [Protagoras, Chapter 30] that the gods had made
      all mortal creatures out of earth and fire. Faust alleges the
      dirtiest of dirt to be a constituent part of Mephistopheles.

19. Am Brunnen

The function of this scene is to reveal the fact of Faust's betrayal
of Gretchen. The time of the action is some days or weeks after
her seduction and before her condition becomes known.

The village well was the usual place for neighborly gossip among
young women; and it was the place too where notices of social
disgrace were usually published by affixing them to a large post
set up for that purpose (the *Brunnensäule*). For example, in Tyrol,
and elsewhere also, the hair of a girl who had had relations with
soldiers or men from other regions was cut off and nailed to the
Brunnensäule.

3544 **Bärbelchen** diminutive of *Barbara*, one of the four great
      virgin saints of the third century (Agnes, Barbara, Catherine,
      and Margaret).

3545 Perhaps because of the conditions stated in lines 3109–3114.
      See also line 3392.

3546 **Sibylle** a woman's name, presumably that of a neighbor.

3548 **Es stinkt** 'something is rotten.'

3560 **Gekos' und Geschleck'** both words with the strong connota-
      tion of vulgarity.

3561 **Blümchen** the symbol of maidenhood.

3569 **Sünderhemdchen**   The law required a girl found guilty of fornication to appear in public in the church, dressed in a sinner's smock, or shift, and to confess the transgression and receive a public reprimand (*deprecatio publica in templo*). Fear of this ordeal led many unwed mothers to kill their illegitimate offspring in an attempt to conceal their guilt. The situation was quite serious in Goethe's day and he had a hand in the abolition of this public expiation in the churches of Weimar by a decree of May 15, 1786.

3572 In another district the young man would not be made to suffer for his wrong-doing, as he would if he remained on the scene.

3574 **soll's** we 'intend that it shall.'

3575 A young woman who bears an illegitimate child may not appear before the altar for her wedding wearing a bridal wreath, and candles before the altar may not be lighted. If she appears with a bridal wreath it will be snatched from her head and torn up by her neighbors.

3576 **Häckerling** Chopped straw or sawdust is scattered before her door. Indeed, a trail of chopped straw is often made from her door to her lover's.

3579 **andrer** genitive plural of the pronoun.

3580 **der Zunge** dative, 'for my tongue to say.'

3581 **schwärzt's** = *ich schwärzte es* 'I made it blacker.'

20. Zwinger

Like the preceding and the following scenes, this is a brief picture revealing Gretchen's soul as her suffering progresses. Several weeks must be assumed to have elapsed. The *Zwinger*, for which there is no single English word, is the narrow space between the town wall and the nearest houses. There is a niche in the town wall in our scene, where a shrine with an image of the Holy Virgin at the cross has been set up.

3587–3588 **neige: Schmerzenreiche** strictly, a case of assonance rather than a pure rime. However, Goethe pronounced the intervocalic -g- without voice and as a spirant (-*ch*-).

3590–3592 These lines refer to the image of the Holy Virgin at the foot of the Cross of Christ. Medieval paintings of the

Mater Dolorosa depict the Holy Virgin with a sword piercing her heart.

3599–3600 **banget, zittert, verlanget** are best taken as intransitives, and *was* as equivalent to *wie*.

3605–3606 The moment she is left alone, she breaks out in weeping.

3608 Outside her windows she keeps potted plants from which she has picked the bouquet she has placed in the vases on the shrine.

21. Nacht

Gretchen's brother has learned of his sister's disgrace. He is lying in wait for her lover, to avenge her betrayal. The dramatic function of this scene is to break off the Gretchen affair by forcing Faust to flee from her town. It adds one more murder to the guilt of the two lovers.

3621 **mag** implies the plausibility of such an occurrence, hence: 'Where, as is quite to be expected, many a man speaks boastfully.'

3624 With a toast to the lady. Supply *haben* with **verschwemmt** and with **gepriesen** 3623.

3625 Valentin did not participate: he was an observer of these boastful harangues.

3633 Like our own: 'Hold a candle to...' the idiom **das Wasser reichen** implies a worthiness to serve another person. The same idea is seen in Mark 1.7 'The latchet of whose shoes I am not worthy to stoop down and unloose.'

3637 Because they could not produce anything to surpass the praise of Gretchen.

3638 'It is enough to make one...'

3648 **er** the betrayer of his sister.

3650 **Sakristei** The vestry is usually located immediately adjacent to the choir of the church and not far from the main altar. Conceivably, though it is certainly not usually the case, the altar lamp, which is kept lighted day and night, might cast some light from a window of the vestry. It is thought of here as a weak shaft of flickering light coming from below upward and casting no light upon the street below the window.

3654 Faust is depressed, Mephistopheles is gleeful. **sieht's** = *sieht's aus* 'things look.'

3656 Villagers and farmers usually kept a ladder handy to permit them quickly to reach their roofs to extinguish fires which might be set by sparks. Cats used these ladders to reach the thatched roofs which were choice hunting and trysting places for feline society.

3658 **tugendlich** To 'feel virtuous' is to feel that one is doing what one should do, that is, that one is *tüchtig*. This is a comfortable feeling and the comfort is really what Mephistopheles means to express: 'I'm quite satisfied with myself.'

3661 **Walpurgisnacht** the night of April 30 to May 1. On that night all witches convene on the *Blocksberg* (the Brocken) and receive their due rewards for services rendered the devil. The name is that of an English nun, Walpurga, who died February 25, 779, as abbess of the Bavarian convent Heidenheim. She became a Saint and her day is May 1. **übermorgen** 3662 indicates that this scene occurs on the night of April 28.

3664–3665 According to popular superstition a buried treasure is revealed to a spirit seer by a phosphorescent glow above its resting place. This one is being elevated to the surface by mysterious unnatural powers. Such a treasure is said to 'bloom' (*der Schatz blüht*). This one is a kettle full of silver coins with the Lion of Bohemia embossed upon them.

3673 Pearls are associated in popular superstition with tears.

3679 **Kunststück** not merely the song that is to be heard, but the cynical trick of using a truly moral song for the accomplishment of quite immoral purposes.

3682–3697 This song has many points of similarity with the Schlegel translation of Ophelia's song in *Hamlet*, IV, 5. The borrowings were cheerfully conceded by Goethe in a conversation with Eckermann, January 18, 1825: "*So singt mein Mephistopheles ein Lied von Shakespeare, und warum sollte er das nicht?*" But it is also instructive to see what Goethe did not borrow: the comparison is easily made.

3684 **Kathrinchen** Catharine was one of the four virgin saints: see note to line 3544.

3693 **Dinger**   This form of the plural is often used to refer to small helpless human beings, or to young, inexperienced girls, as here.

3698 **Element**   See note to line 2805.

3699 **Rattenfänger**   Either an allusion to the Pied Piper of Hameln or a reminiscence of *Romeo and Juliet*, III, 1, where Mercutio calls Tybalt a rat-catcher.

3703 Supply a verb of motion: "*Nun soll es . . . gehen.*" 'Now we shall proceed . . .'

3704 **gewichen**, like *zugestoßen* 3707 a past participle used in a command. This usage is most frequent in short, sharp commands or warnings.

3711 **zahm** 'no longer dangerous.'

3714 **Polizei: Blutbann**   With the former, which deals with crimes other than murder, Mephistopheles can deal. With the latter, which deals with matters of life and death, he cannot. The most likely reason would appear to be that this court requires imperial sanction and the Emperor is looked on as the instrument of God. Mephistopheles says he has no means of controlling decrees arrived at in the Emperor's name or on his behalf.

3720 By calling Valentin 'Your mother's son' rather than 'Your brother' the crowd indicates its abhorrence of the fallen Gretchen. Stage directors usually make the crowd show their revulsion by turning away from Gretchen.

3732 **Was soll mir das?**   'Such words to me?' or 'What's all this going to come to?' (*Was soll mir das bedeuten?*)

3737 **mehre** an inflected form of *mehr*. In older German this word was occasionally inflected when used as a pronoun but it is now invariable, *mehr*.

3740–3744 These lines prefigure the birth and destruction of the illegitimate child.

3752 **Leichen** an old dative singular form in *–n*.

3754 **soll** expresses the will of the speaker.

3756 Valentin lists a few of the penalties his sister is to suffer, all of them in accordance with the laws and customs of the time.

Young women of ill repute were forbidden by local or church law to wear golden jewelry, to participate in church services, and to wear fine clothes in public places.

3760 **Jammerecken** is an older accusative singular of *–ecke*, which has now gone out of use in Standard German.

3765 **Lästrung** The blasphemy is implied in his curse of Gretchen despite the possibility that God forgives her (3762–3763).

3766 Supply *kommen* 'If I could only get ...'

3767 This is a direct accusation of Marthe's complicity in Gretchen's fall.

3769 **reiche Maß** In modern German, **Maß** is regularly a neuter noun.

3772 **der Ehre** genitive singular with *lossprechen*.

22. Dom

The function of this scene is to indicate forcefully the growing anguish of the desperate girl. The evil spirit who speaks here is Gretchen's own consciousness of sin, her bad conscience, personified as a demon, probably analogous to the evil spirit of Jehovah, I. Samuel 16, 14, who plagued Saul.

3779 **Büchelchen** her prayer-book, handed down from generation to generation and hence well-worn.

3786 The evil spirit reminds Gretchen of her mother's death, her brother's death, and her illegitimate child.

3788 **Pein** in purgatory, because she died unshriven in her sleep and so without benefit of extreme unction.

3795 **Gedanken** genitive plural with *los*. Modern usage requires the accusative.

3797 **wider mich** 'In spite of all I can do.'

3798 This famous Latin hymn, written as a mass for the dead, can be found with a German translation in Karl Simrock's *Lauda Sion*, Stuttgart, 1868 (2nd. ed., p. 333). Goethe quotes directly from the first, sixth, and seventh of the seventeen stanzas, and alludes to the content of the third and fourth. The first two lines go: 'Day of wrath, that day will change the world into cinders.'

3800 **Grimm**   The wrath of the day of judgment (*dies irae*).

3801   The trumpet, I. Corinthians 15.52: '. . . at the last trump, for
the trumpet shall sound and the dead shall be raised incorruptible.'   In the hymn:

> Tuba mirum spargens sonum
> Per sepulcra regionum
> Coget omnes ante thronum.

> 'The war-trumpet casting its astonishing sound
> Through the sepulchres of the lands
> Summons everyone (to appear) before the throne (of
> God).'

3803–3807   Instead of being raised up incorruptible to dwell forever
with God, as St. Paul promised the Corinthians and the
Thessalonians, Gretchen is now told that she will rise from
her grave to suffer the torments of flaming Hell.   Even such
peace as her heart will meanwhile find in the grave is de-
cribed as a 'peace of ashes' (*Aschenruh*).

3811   'As if the song would break my heart.'

3813   'For when the judge shall hold court,
Whatever is hidden will appear publicly;
Nothing will remain unavenged.'

3822 **bleibt**   A singular verb with a compound subject which is
thought of as a single unit.

3825   'What then am I, wretched one, to say?
What patron am I then to implore,
When scarcely the just man is secure?'

3829 **Verklärte**   Transfigured souls (see I. Corinthians 15.51) who
have risen from their graves (see I. Thessalonians 4.16).
These turn away from the sinful soul.

3834 **Fläschchen** of smelling salts.   In the days when women fainted
frequently in public places most of them carried a little
bottle containing an aromatic preparation of carbonate of
ammonia, usually with some perfume added, the vapor from
which they inhaled when they felt faint.

23. *Walpurgisnacht*

The scene is the top of the Brocken Mountain in the Harz, where the witches are gathered on the *Blocksberg* for Walpurga's Night. Among the many adventures of Faust and Mephistopheles on this wild night we have chosen to present only a short incident which is related to the Gretchen episode. Faust sees a phantom which looks to him like Gretchen.

4194 The Gorgon **Medusa**, a terrible monster in Greek mythology, who laid waste the country of Polydectes. This monster had once been a very beautiful maiden whose chief glory was her hair. But Minerva, who found the girl's beauty troublesome, transformed the curls of her hair into hissing serpents and made her so horrible to look upon that any living thing which did so was turned to stone.

4197 It is precisely opposite to Mephistopheles' plans that Faust should see Gretchen's form in this phantom on the Blocksberg. He hastens to assure Faust that it is not Gretchen, but sheer hocus-pocus: a phantom that appears to every man as his sweetheart.

4207 The most noted of the dead who are thus able to walk about with their heads under their arms is probably Bertrand de Born. Another is Anne Boleyn.

4208 **Perseus** was sent out by Polydectes to attempt to destroy the Medusa. He skillfully used his shining shield as a mirror, so that he might approach the monster without looking at her. When he found her either asleep or in prayer, one is not certain which, he chopped off her head. The image of Medusa's head was embossed on the shield of Minerva (Pallas Athena).

4209 Faust is still fascinated by this vision which looks to him like Gretchen and which Mephistopheles calls a delusion (**Wahn**). The devil's purpose is ill suited by a return of Faust's thoughts to the kind of love represented by his experience with Gretchen.

25. *Trüber Tag. Feld.*

When Goethe first read this scene to his circle of friends at the court of Weimar it made a deep impression upon them because of the consuming rage of Goethe as he read Faust's attack upon Mephistopheles. It is the only scene of the play which has remained in its original prose form. Goethe planned to put it into verse, as

he did the prison scene, but it is clear that the elemental passion of
Faust here could not be confined to a strict metrical form.

Somehow Faust has learned that Gretchen is now in prison after
having fled or been driven from her home and having wandered
about the countryside in her misery.   Without ceremony we are
plunged immediately into the midst of Faust's tirade against
Mephistopheles, and indeed against himself as well.   The dramatic
function of the scene is to show Faust's return to his nobler self
and his determination to risk everything in an attempt to alleviate
the suffering he has caused.

TT 2 **lange** The time factor is ambiguous.   Presumably Faust
fled from Gretchen's neighborhood immediately after the
murder of Valentin.   How much time intervened between
this and the time of the present scene is not indicated, but it
can hardly have been very long.

TT 4 **Bis dahin** (*ist es gekommen!*)

TT 5–6 Mephistopheles is trying to walk away from his master.

TT 9 **Bösen Geistern** such as the one of the cathedral scene, see
the introductory note to Scene 22, *Dom.*

TT 15 Any demon or evil spirit, which for one reason or another
had to serve a human being, quite commonly appeared in
the form of a dog.   Mephistopheles is here said to have so
appeared to Faust on many an evening walk.   Indeed, it was
the favorite form of this spirit.

TT 24–26 Faust speaks from the premise that vicarious expiation
of sin is just, and he may be assumed still to believe that guilt
can be expiated in the sight of God.   He cannot understand
why the deep misery of the first girl to suffer as Gretchen is
suffering should not have expiated the guilt of all other such
transgressors in the eyes of God.

TT 32–33 People who wish to fly should be secure against attacks
of dizziness: people who associate with demons should be
secure against attacks of conscience.

TT 44–45 Mephistopheles cannot control the decrees of the court
which deals with murder, because the decrees of that court
are given 'in God's name.'   See also note to lines 3714–3715.
— Gretchen has been found guilty of the murder of her
infant child.

TT 47 **Donner** an allusion to the god, Jupiter, who hurled thunderbolts at those who displeased him.

TT 53 **Blutschuld** By the murder of Valentin blood-guilt has been put upon the city or state, which is obliged then by law to remove this blood-guilt by bringing the murderer to his due punishment.

TT 55 **rächende Geister** Analogous to the Furies of ancient Greece.

26. *Nacht. Offen Feld*

The time, presumably, is in the night following *Trüber Tag*. As Faust and Mephistopheles approach their destination they look down and see a group of figures in an open field.

4399 **Rabenstein** The raven's stone was a block or platform of masonry built beneath a gallows, or used as a platform for the decapitation of convicted criminals. Hence the word often means a place of execution. This is the spot where in the morning Gretchen is to be executed for killing her child.

4403 The reference is to gestures of these spirits. Mephistopheles says they are witches, and most commentators accept this description. Others, however, believe that these are friendly spirits, preparing to receive Gretchen's soul.

27. *Kerker*

The scene shows Faust, first outside the prison, and then in the cell in which Gretchen is chained. The function of the scene is to present the denouement of the Gretchen tragedy and the end of one phase of the Faust drama.

4405 Faust is once more accessible to the sentiment of compassion and love for human-kind.

4408 **Verbrechen** not the murder of her child, but its ultimate cause: her yielding to Faust's urgings of love and to her own natural, hence good, impulses, in the belief that anything so good must also be right (3585–3586).

4411 **Fort** 'Forward.'

4412–4420 This song, sung by Gretchen, somewhat as the distraught Ophelia sings in *Hamlet* (Act IV, Scene 5), demonstrates the pathological condition of Gretchen's mind. The text of the song suggests the song of the bird in the *Märchen von dem Machandelbaum* (Grimm):

> My mother, who killed me!
> My father, who ate me!
> My sister, little Marlene,
> Hunted and found all my little bones;
> She wrapped them up in a silken cloth
> And laid them away under the juniper tree. —
> Keewitt! Keewitt!
> What a fine (lovely) bird I am now!

4423 **Sie** as Gretchen thinks, the servants of the executioner, come to take her to the *Rabenstein*. She does not recognize Faust until line 4470, and even then but dully.

4436 **Kranz** that is, *Mädchenkranz*, *Jungfernkranz*. Every bride hoped to appear before the altar for her wedding wearing a bridal wreath signifying her maidenhood. Gretchen's wreath here may be taken as the symbol of the maidenhood she had lost. See also 3561.

4443 A hallucination. Her child is dead.

4449–4450 'There is an old tale that ends with a girl's killing her own child. Who bids them apply that tale to me?'

4460 There is a popular belief that a person who walks in his sleep will promptly wake up upon hearing his given name spoken. Faust arouses Gretchen from her distraught condition by calling out her name.

4475 Even before she can take a step to escape, Gretchen is overcome by the sweet memories of a happy past. This is a demonstration of the insuperable power of her love impulse.

4493 Faust is no longer driven by his overpowering love for this girl, but by his sense of guilt and his sense of duty to expiate this guilt. There is no fire of love in his lips now and Gretchen infers at once that some other girl has stolen him from her.

4512–4517 Another hallucination. She thinks Faust's hand is wet with the blood of her brother, that he is still there in the street, sword in hand, after slaying Valentin.

4520–4529 In her imagination the tragic events are all brought together in time, so that the burial of all the victims is to be attended to in the morning.

4538–4541 Gretchen has prepared herself to die in the first hours of the dawn. She cannot accept a change in this idea. She will go with Faust, if to do so is to go to death with him, not otherwise.

4545 **Sie** the representatives of state and church, the officers of the law.

4551 Another hallucination. Gretchen thinks she is leading Faust to the rescue of the child she had drowned.

4565 Now Gretchen's mind turns to the death of her mother and the condition in which she found her on the morning after she had given her the sleeping potion.

4567 Gretchen thinks she feels something (*es*) seize her by the hair of her head. Such a hallucination is the result of her anticipation of this sensation as a part of her coming execution. The line is parenthetical and probably derived chiefly from the exigencies of rime, yet the very disjuncture of the imagery suits the mental state of distraction here depicted.

4583 For the explanation of the **Kranz** see note to 4436.

4590 The ringing of the *Armesünderglocke*, which tolls while the condemned is being led to the place of execution. The rod is broken above the head of the condemned as a symbol of the death decree of the court. Before each execution, the court decree which orders it is read, and the judge, or his representative, breaks a small white wand as indicated.

4593–4594 An allusion to the fact that every witness of an execution by the axe so far identifies himself with the victim as to feel, momentarily at least, that the knife is falling on his own neck.

4595 She thinks the blow has fallen so that she hears nothing.

4599 These horses will disappear into thin air with the first ray of the dawn or the first crowing of the cock.

4603 **heilig** Because she has resigned herself to God's judgment and this has brought her here, she calls the place sacred. Then too, any prison is an asylum against pursuers bent on doing harm to a fugitive or prisoner.

4606 Mephistopheles is desperate. He threatens to leave Faust to suffer arrest and execution along with Gretchen, because he cannot himself submit to arrest by human hands.

4609 An allusion to Psalm 34.7: 'The angel of Jehovah encampeth round about them that fear him, and delivereth them.'

4610 Margarete's terror of her lover results from her determination to follow God's judgment and her conviction that Faust is not a part thereof. The conviction crystallizes when she sees Mephistopheles again with Faust (see lines 3493–3500).

4611 This voice of God (in the stage direction) is a part of the traditional folk-drama of Faust, here used by Goethe to balance the verdict of Mephistopheles. Gretchen is not to be thought of as condemned to Hell. She has cast herself on God's mercy.

4612 Mephistopheles drags the dazed Faust away, but Gretchen's voice still reaches him. It is the voice of love which will not pass away.

Vocabulary

When the forms occurring in the text require it, we give noun plurals and verb morphology. Such separable compound verbs as occur separated in the text are cross-referred from the verb entry to the prefix entry.

A

ab downward, off; exit, exeunt; leave(s) the stage

der **Abend** evening

aber but, however

abfallen fall off, drop off

sich **abfinden** make arrangements, get along

abgehen go down

abgeschmackt in bad taste, insipid, absurd

der **Abgrund** precipice, abyss

ablegen (*wk*) bear (witness)

abscheulich horrible, loathsome

abschlagen (ä), u, a strike off, cut off

abschweben float down, soar down

abspazieren (*wk*) stroll away, stroll down

abtreiben, ie, ie jade, drive to the point of exhaustion

abwenden turn away

abwischen wipe dry

abzupfen pluck off

ach ah, alas, oh

acht: sich in acht nehmen take care, be careful (not to)

Ade! good-bye

affenjung very young, inexperienced; **affenjunges Blut** very young and inexperienced creature

ah! ah

ahnen have an idea, suspect, be aware of

der **Ahnherr** ancestor, founder of a family

der **Ahnungsdrang** intuitive impulse

ahnungsvoll intuitive; sinister, ominous, foreboding

akkurat exacting, accurate

all all, every, all the; universal; everything, everyone

allein(e) lone, alone, solitary; solus; only; however, but

allemal: ein für allemal once and for all, under all circumstances

der **Allerhalter** Preserver of the universe

allerlei all kinds of

allerorten everywhere

allerwegs under all circumstances

allerweit'ste broadest

allgemein general, universal

allmächtig almighty, omnipotent

der **Allumfasser** Encompasser of the universe

allzuviele excessive

das **Alpenfeld** Alpine field, meadow
als as, as if, like (3475); when; than; but, except
alt old, ancient
der **Altar** altar
altvergraben long buried
am = an dem
das **Amt** mass (3776)
an at, by, along, near, up to, on, with, in; to (2855)
anbinden: kurz angebunden brusque, snappish
der **Anblick** sight, view
anbrechen (i) fall (*night*)
das **Andachtsbild** image in a shrine
ander other, different, second; else
anders otherwise, else, different(ly)
anderwärts elsewhere
anfangen (ä), i, a begin, undertake, do
anfassen take hold of, seize, grasp
anfüllen (*wk*) fill up, occupy
das **Angedenken** memento, keepsake
angehen be practicable; concern
das **Angesicht** face, countenance
die **Angst** terror, anxiety
ängsten distress
anhören listen to
anklopfen knock at the door
ankommen, a, o depend
der **Anlaß** occasion
anlegen put on
annehmen accept
sich **annehmen** (i), a, o take an interest in
anriechen discover by smelling
anrufen call upon, invoke
ans = an das
anschaffen (*wk*) procure
ansehen look at
anstatt instead of
anstecken (*wk*) infect, taint
der **Anteil** interest
die **Antipathie** antipathy

das **Antlitz** countenance
der **Antonius** Anthony
antragen offer
die **Antwort** answer
anwandeln come over
der **Appetit** appetite
arg bad; **ärger** worse
der **Arm** –e arm
arm poor
armselig miserable, wretched
die **Armut** poverty
die **Art** kind, sort, type; manner, style, way
die **Aschenruh** peace of death (*ashes, dust*)
der **Atem** breath
atmen breathe
auch also, too, likewise; even; either; (**was, wer, wenn**) . . . **auch** . . . -ever
auf on, upon; in response to; in, at, to, for, up, up to; get up! **auf und ab, auf und nieder** up and down, back and forth
aufbeben rise trembling
aufbewahren (*wk*) preserve, keep
aufbinden fasten up, tie up
aufblicken look up, glance up
aufdämmern dawn, grow light
sich **aufdringen**, a, u intrude upon, force oneself upon
auffliegen, o, o fly off, take wing
auffressen (i), a, e devour, engorge
aufgehen go up
aufheben, u, o lift up; lay away
auflauern lie in wait for
aufmachen open
aufmerksam becoming aware
aufnehmen (i), a, o receive, accept
aufputzen dress up, deck out; adjust (*another's*) finery
aufreiben, ie, ie wear out, exhaust

aufschaffen, u, a revive (*to further torture*)
aufschauen look, look up
aufschließen unlock
aufschweben float up, soar up; **auf- und abschweben** soar up and down
aufschwellen distend, swell
aufsitzen, a, e sit up
aufspringen jump up
aufstehen get up, arise, stand up
aufstemmen (*wk*) prop up; **den Ellenbogen aufgestemmt** leaning on one's elbow
auftreten (i) enter, appear
aufwärts upward
aufzehren consume
aufziehen, o, o bring up, raise
das **Auge, –n** eye
der **Augenblick** moment, instant
das **Augenblickchen** fleeting instant
aus out of, from, because of, for
ausbilden (*wk*) form, bring to perfection
auserlesen made to order, selected
ausführlich in detail
der **Ausgang** way out, exit
aushalten (ä) endure
auslachen laugh at, ridicule
ausraufen tear out
ausrecken (*wk*) stretch out
ausrupfen pluck off
aussehen (ie), a, e seem, appear
sich **aussetzen** expose oneself to
ausspüren trace, trail, track down
austeilen distribute, give
sich **ausweinen** (*wk*) cry one's heart out
sich **ausziehen** undress

B

der **Bach** brook
das **Bächlein** brooklet

bald soon; nearly; **bald ... bald** now ... now
baldig early
das **Band** ribbon (2788)
das **Band, –e** bond (Trüber Tag 44)
bang uneasy, nervous, fearful, anxious
bangen be disturbed, be disquieted
das **Bärbelchen** Barbara, "Babs"
barsch rude, impolite
der **Bart** beard
der **Bauch** belly
beben tremble, quake
–beben *see* aufbeben
der **Becher** goblet, chalice
bedauern pity
bedenken consider, reflect, bear in mind
der **Beding** condition, stipulation
befangen (ä) imprison (3818); **= befangen machen** trouble, confuse, perplex (2824)
befehlen commend, entrust
befreien free, set free, liberate
begegnen meet, encounter
begehren (*wk*) request, wish, desire, hanker after, crave, long for, covet
die **Begier** craving, appetite
begierig eager, hungry
beginnen, a (begonnte 3176), o begin, undertake; be active
das **Beginnen** activity
begraben (ä), u, a bury
begreifen comprehend, understand
behagen suit, fit, give pleasure to, please
behalten (ä): **recht behalten** be right; win an argument
bei in connection with, with, by, at the house of, near, in case of, during
die **Beichte** confession
beide both, two
beidrängen press, crowd
beim = bei dem
das **Bein, –e** leg; bone (4417)

beiseite

beiseite aside, to one side

beizeiten betimes, in time

bejammern bewail, mourn

bekehren convert; dissuade

bekennen admit, acknowledge, confess

bekommen, a, o agree with; **Lust bekommen** think one would like to

belehren instruct, advise, teach; **mich eines Besseren belehren** make me change my mind

belieben please, seem desirable

belohnen reward

sich **bemächtigen** take possession

beneiden (*wk*) envy

sich **bequemen** adapt oneself, conform, submit, lower oneself

sich **beraten** deliberate, make plans

bereit ready, in readiness

bereuen (*wk*) regret, feel remorse for

der **Berg, -e** hill, mountain

der **Beruf** activity, function, calling

sich **berühmen** boast

berühren touch

beschämen (*wk*) shame, make ashamed, disconcert

beschimpfen insult, call names

beschreiben describe

sich **besinnen** reflect, think, think over

besser better

beste best; dearest

bestürzt thrown into confusion, dismayed

der **Besuch** visit; company, visitor

betauen (*wk*) bedew

beten (*wk*) pray, offer a prayer

betören (*wk*) delude, fool, make a fool of, bedazzle, seduce

das **Betragen** behavior, conduct

betrauern (*wk*) be in mourning for

betreffen (i), **a, o** surprise

betrüben (*wk*) grieve, afflict, cause sorrow

das **Bett** bed

betteln beg

der **Bettler, —** beggar

der **Bettvorhang** bed curtain

sich **beugen** bend, bow

bewahren preserve, guard

bewegen move, stir, set in motion, excite, agitate

sich **bewegen** move

bezeugen make a declaration

bieten, o, o offer

—**bilden** *see* ausbilden, einbilden

binden bind

sich **binden, a, u** put oneself under obligations

bis until, up to, as far as, to the point of, all the way to

ein **bißchen** a little, a bit, a little bit, somewhat, rather

die **Bitte** request, petition

bitten, a, e ask, ask for, entreat, beg

bitter bitter

blaß pale

das **Blatt, ⸚er** leaf; petal (3179)

bleiben stay, stay behind, remain, continue to be; always will be

der **Blick, -e** glance, look; view, vision, spectacle, sight

blicken look, glance

—**blicken** *see* aufblicken, umherblicken

bloß bare; openly (3746); **der Sünde bloß** vulnerable because of my own transgression (3584)

das **Blümchen** flower (*of maidenhood* 3561)

die **Blume, -n** flower

der **Blumenkrug, ⸚e** vase, flower jar

das **Blumenwort** flower's word

das **Blut** blood; spirits; **junges Blut** young creature

der **Blutbann** criminal court

die **Blutschuld** blood guilt

der **Blutstuhl** executioner's block

der **Boden** ground; floor

bös bad, evil, wicked, harsh, unkind, angry

der **Brauch** custom, usage

brauchen (*wk*) need, require

brausen (*wk*) rage, roar

brav good, decent, upright, well-behaved, honest, fine, valiant

bravo! bravo

brechen (i), a, o break; pluck off (*flower*)

–**brechen** *see* anbrechen

der **Brei** porridge, mush

breit broad, wide

breiten spread, broaden

brennen burn, blaze, be on fire

das **Brimborium** elaborate nonsense

bringen, a, a (*wk, irreg*) bring; **bringen** (**um**) deprive of (4497)

–**bringen** *see* herbringen, hinbringen, umbringen

das **Brot** bread

der **Bruder** brother

der **Brunnen** fountain, well

brünstig ardent

die **Brust, ⁻e** bosom, breast, chest; heart

der **Bube, –n** boy

das **Büchelchen** prayer book

die **Buhle** sweetheart, paramour (*female*)

der **Buhle, –n** lover, sweetheart (*male*)

das **Bund** bunch, bundle

Bürgersleute townspeople

der **Busen** bosom, breast; heart; mind

büßen expiate, atone for, suffer for

C

der **Chor** chorus, choir

der **Christ** Christian

der **Christ: der heilige Christ** Christmas present

das **Christentum** Christian faith

D

da (*conj*) when, since

da (*adv*) then, there, here; in that respect, in such a case, under those circumstances

dabei present; with that; participating; in that connection, at the same time

dadrinne at home (there in the city)

dafür in return for that, to make up for that; for it; for that

daherbrausen come roaring along

dahin to there, to that place, into that place

dahinaus out there

damals at that time, then

damit (*conj*) so that

damit (*adv*) with that, with it, with them; by that; thereby; with which

dämmern grow faint, grow dim (*light*)

–**dämmern** *see* aufdämmern

der **Dämmerschein** dusk

der **Dank** thanks, gratitude

dankbar thankful, grateful

danken (*wk*) thank, give thanks, be grateful for

dann then, at that time; thereafter

darauf on that

daraus out of it

darneben beside, next, next to it

darüber: darüber gehen surpass it in value

darum about that, concerning that

das the, that, that one, it; which

daß that; so that

dastehen, a (ü), a stand there

davon of that, about that, from that; away (Trüber Tag 66)

davor before it

dazu for that, to that, to do that; in addition

die **Definition, –en** definition

der **Degen** sword

dein your, yours, of you

um **deinetwillen** for your sake

die **Demut** humility

denken, a, a (*wk, irreg*) think, intend, plan, imagine, realize

denn (*conj*) for, because (*justifying previous remark*)

denn (*adv*) in that case, then (*implying uncertainty as to the reply*)

der the, that, that one; he, it; who, which

derweil meanwhile

deucht (dünken) seems

deuten interpret, explain

die the, that, that one, those; she, her, it, they, them; who, whom, which

der **Dieb** thief

das **Diebsgelüst** desire to steal, kleptomania

der **Dienst** service, good turn

dienstlich of service, useful

dies this, this latter, the latter

das **Ding, –e/–er** thing, creature; **es geht nicht mit rechten Dingen zu** there's something wrong about this, things like this don't happen by proper means

die **Dirne** wench, girl

doch though, after all, yet, still, in spite of that, however, on the contrary; **nicht doch** Oh no; not at all

der **Doktor** doctor, PhD

der **Dom** cathedral

der **Donner** thunder; thunderbolt

das **Dorf** village

dort there, at that place

dran doing that; of that, from that, on it, in that, to that; off (3149); **dran kommen** take one's turn

drängen press, throng, crowd together

sich **drängen** crowd, press

–drängen *see* beidrängen, hindrängen

drauf in addition, to that; forthwith, immediately

drauß outside

draußen outside, out there

der **Dreck** filth

drei three

dreihundert three hundred

drein in it

dreinsehen (ie) have an expression on one's face (2748, 3486); look, present an appearance (2797)

drin therein, within, inside

dringen, a, u press, force a way; urge

–dringen *see* aufdringen, hereindringen

drinne inside, in there, in town

droben up there, on high

der **Druck** pressure

drücken press, squeeze, clasp

–drücken *see* zudrücken

drum so, therefore; for it (2678, 2915, 4517); of it (4497)

du you (thou)

ducken yield, conform, submit

sich **ducken** stoop, humble oneself; duck, dodge

dumpf moist; dull; still scarcely aroused (3352)

dumpfig musty

dunkel dark

(es) **dünkelt ihm** he conceitedly imagines

dünken, eu, eu (*irreg, impers*) seem

der **Dunstkreis** region filled by sweet fragrance; aura of fragrance

durch through; by means of

durchführen carry through

durchs = durch das

durchweben weave through

durchwühlen stir to the depths, burrow through

dürfen (a), u, u (*irreg*) be allowed to, may, can, dare; **nicht dürfen** must not; **es durfte kaum** it needed scarcely (3139)

dürr dry, dried-up

das **Dutzend** dozen

E

eben precisely, just, neither more nor less than, exactly; simply; when all is said and done; the point is that

ebenfalls likewise, too

das **Ebenholz** ebony

die **Ecke** corner

edel noble, high-born, aristocratic

die **Edelfrau** noblewoman

die **Ehe** marriage

ehe before

eher sooner, more easily, rather

der **Ehherr** husband

die **Ehre**, –n honor, glory; good reputation; **in allen Ehren** with all due respect

ehren honor, respect, revere

ehrerbietig respectful, deferential

die **Ehrfurcht** awe, awed respect

ehrlos brazen, shameless

ei! well! why! ay! indeed! but ...!

eigen of one's own

eilen hurry, hurry up

ein a, an; one

ein in; **aus und ein** in and out

sich **einbilden** (*wk*) imagine, flatter oneself; be vain

die **Einfalt** artless simplicity

eingeboren innate, inborn; born

eingehen enter; go in

einige several, some

einlassen (ä) let in, admit

einmal once, one time, some

time; even, after all; **auf einmal** all at once; **nicht einmal** not even; **noch einmal** again; **ein für allemal** once and for all (2656); **laßt einmal** just wait

einnehmen capture, occupy

einräumen put away

einschlurfen sip

sich **einschränken** restrain oneself, be economical

einsehen (ie) perceive, see, get the point

einsperren (*wk*) imprison

einstecken sheathe

einstreichen, i, i pocket

einteufeln (*wk*) initiate into the ways of the Devil

eintreten (i) enter

einzig unique, single

eisern iron

die **Eitelkeit** vanity

ekeln disgust, nauseate

das **Element** element; **beim Element** (an oath)

elend miserable, wretched

das **Elend** misery

der **Ellenbogen** elbow

empfangen (ä), i, a receive, welcome

empfinden, a, u feel, experience, perceive

das **Ende** end, death

endigen end; finish, be through

endlich finally, at last

eng narrow, restricted; **es wird ihr eng** she begins to feel oppressed

der **Engel**, — angel

der **Engelsschatz** beloved; my sweet angel

ennuyieren bore

entbehren do without

entfernen (*wk*) separate

entfliehen, o, o desert, run away, escape

entführen carry off

entgegenfletschen grin at, bare one's teeth at

entgegnen offer objection; make a reply
entlang along
entrücken (*wk*) carry off, carry away
entsetzlich horrible
entstehen arise
sich entwirken (*wk*) work itself out, evolve
entwohnt unaccustomed, once known but now unfamiliar
entzücken delight, enchant; zum Entzücken delightful, enchanting
entzünden set ablaze, inflame
entzwei in two, broken apart
er he, it; Er you
das Erbarmen pity
sich erbarmen pity, have pity, have mercy
erbärmlich pitiable
erbauen (*wk*) edify
der Erbe, –n heir
erbeten ask for and receive
erblicken see, catch sight of
der Erdball terrestrial globe
die Erde earth, world, earthly life; ground, soil
der Erdensohn son of earth, earthling
erfahren (ä), u, a experience
erfreuen delight
erfüllen fill, fill up
ergehen, i, a happen, turn out
ergreifen lay hold of, seize, grasp
ergrimmt angry
erhalten (ä) preserve, uphold; maintain
sich erholen (*wk*) recover
die Erinnrung memory, remembrance, recollection
erkennen, a, a (*wk*, *irreg*) recognize, perceive, understand
erleben experience
ermorden murder
der Ernst a matter of serious importance; im Ernste seriously

eröffnen open
erscheinen appear
erschlagen (ä), u, a kill, slay
erst first, foremost; wenn erst as soon as, once; when ... first
erstarren stiffen, solidify, congeal
das erstemal first time
ersticken smother, stifle
ertränken (*wk*) drown
erwachen (*wk*) awake, waken
erwarmen become warm
erweisen show
erzählen tell about, tell
erziehen, o, o bring up, rear
es it, someone, people; there
essen (i), a, e (gessen) eat
das Essen food, eating
etwa by any chance, perhaps
etwas something, anything; somewhat, rather; so etwas anything like that
Euch (*sg*) euch (*pl*) you, to you, for you
euer your, yours, of you
euresgleichen the like(s) of you, your kind
ewig eternal, everlasting; forever

F

fabeln (*wk*) talk wildly, be delirious
–fahren *see* fortfahren
das Fahrzeug vehicle, ship (2974)
fallen (ä) fall
–fallen *see* abfallen
falsch false
fangen (ä), i, a catch, imprison, capture
–fangen *see* anfangen
fassen (*wk*) lay hold on, take hold of; take, seize, grasp; understand, encompass; contain; Mut fassen take heart
–fassen *see* anfassen
fast almost

Faust Faust, Faustus
fechten (i) fight, fence
fegen sweep
fehlen go astray
der Fehler, — mistake
der Feiertag holiday
fein fine; delicate, artful, deft
das Feld field
das Fell, skin, hide
der Fels, –en rock, rocky cliff
die Felsenritze, –n rocky crevice
das Fenster window
fern(e) far, far-off, remote, distant
die Fessel, –n fetter
fest firm, solid
das Fest festival, holiday, feast
feucht moist, damp, wet
das Feuer fire
die Feuerleiter, –n fire ladder
finden, a, u find, discover; consider, think
der Finger finger
die Fingerspitze finger tip
finster dark, gloomy, dim
die Finsternis darkness, shadow(s)
die Flammenqual, –en fiery torment
flämmern flicker
das Fläschchen small bottle; bottle of smelling salts (3834)
flechten braid, plait
der Flederwisch feather duster (= rapier)
flehen implore, beseech, pray
–fletschen *see* entgegenfletschen
fliegen, o, o fly
–fliegen *see* fortfliegen
fliehen flee, take flight
flimmern glimmer, glitter
flink brisk, lively
der Flor flower
der Fluch curse, a curse
fluchen curse
der Flüchtling fugitive
der Flügel, — wing
die Flut flood, waters, sea
folgen follow

förderlich useful, helpful
fördern: Will's fördern? Are you getting anywhere?
fort away; go away; continuously; immer fort always
fortgehen go away
fortfahren (ä) continue
fortfliegen fly away
sich fortmachen take oneself off, begone
fortreisen travel on
fortschicken send away
fortstreben strive to get away
fragen ask, inquire
der Frager questioner
der Franzos Frenchman
die Frau, –en woman; wife; lady; Mrs.
das Fräulein, –s young lady
frech insolent, bold, impudent, shameless
die Frechheit boldness
frei free, released, uninhibited, relaxed, comfortable and happy
das Freie out of doors, open, clear
der Freier suitor
die Freiheit freedom, liberty
freisprechen (i), a, o absolve from
fremd foreign, not one's own, someone else's, strange, unfamiliar
die Fremde foreign lands
–fressen *see* hineinfressen
die Freude, –n joy, delight; pleasure
freuen give pleasure, make happy
sich freuen (*wk*) be happy, be glad, enjoy oneself
der Freund, –e friend, lover
freundlich friendly, kind, cheerful
der Frevel evil deed, sin and crime
der Friede peace; in Frieden undisturbed
frisch fresh; vigorous, brisk
froh happy, joyous

fromm devout, pious; gentle, good
früh early
fühlen feel
sich **fühlen** feel, feel oneself
führen (*wk*) lead; conduct, bear, carry, bring, take; **das Leben führen** live, spend one's life
–führen *see* herausführen, hinführen
die **Fülle** abundance, fullness
für for, for the sake of; **für sich** for oneself, to oneself, aside
furchtbar awful, fearful
fürchten fear, be afraid of
fürchterlich frightful
furchtsam timid, easily frightened
fürliebnehmen put up with what one finds
fürwahr forsooth, indeed
der **Fuß, ⸚e** foot
füttern feed

G

die **Gabe, –n** gift, talent
gaffen gape, stare (at)
der **Galan** lover, paramour
der **Gang** corridor, passageway, path; bearing, gait
ganz whole, entire, complete, total, all; quite, altogether
gar quite, absolutely; at all; very; even; really
garstig nasty, ugly
das **Gärtchen** little garden
der **Garten** garden
das **Gartenhäuschen** garden summerhouse
die **Gasse, –n** (narrow) street
der **Gaul** horse
die **Gebärde** gesture
gebären, a, o bear, give birth to; **geboren** born
das **Gebein** bones
geben (i), a, e give, present; inflict, produce, cause; **es gibt** there is/are; goes on;

verloren geben give up as lost; **es gibt sich** it does happen
das **Gebet, –e** prayer
das **Gebetbuch** prayer book
das **Gebirg, –e** mountain, mountain range
sich **gebühren** (*wk*) be fitting, be right and proper
der **Gedanke, –n** thought; revery
gedeihen thrive, prosper
die **Gefahr** danger
gefallen (ä) appeal, please
sich **gefallen** (ä), ie, a take pleasure
gefällig pleasing, agreeable
gefräßig greedy
das **Gefühl** feeling, emotion
gefühllos heartless, unfeeling
die **Gegenwart** presence
das **Geheimnis** mystery
gehen, i, a go, walk; come; happen, proceed, work; go away; **darüber gehen** exceed it in value; **zugrunde gehen** be destroyed; **gehen und stehen** go along somehow, be possible, be
–gehen *see* abgehen, angehen, aufgehen, eingehen, fortgehen, herübergehen, herumgehen, hineingehen, hinübergehen, übergehen, vorbeigehen, vorübergehen, weggehen, zugehen
gehören belong
der **Geist, –er** spirit, soul
geizig avaricious
das **Gekose** continual petting
das **Gelag** revel, drinking bout
gelassen calm, serene, composed
geläufig customary, easy
das **Geld** money
die **Gelegenheit** opportunity, occasion
gelegentlich occasionally, when opportunity offers
das **Geleit** escort; **Geleit antragen** offer to escort

geleiten escort, accompany

der Geliebte loved one, beloved

gelingen prosper, turn out well; es gelingt mir I succeed; I can, it is possible for me gelt! don't you think?

die Gemeinschaft common cause

genau exacting, strict

das Genie genius; demonic spirit (3540)

genießen, o, o enjoy, partake, take one's pleasure (in)

genug enough, sufficient

genung = genug

das Gerede gossip; ins Gerede kommen get talked about

das Gericht court of justice, judgment

gern(e) like to, gladly, eagerly, willingly

der Geruch sense of smell

der Gesang song

geschehen (ie), a, e take place, happen, befall; geschehen sein have happened, be all over

gescheit clever

das Geschenk, -e present, gift

die Geschichte story

das Geschick fate

das Geschlecht sex

das Geschlecke continual kissing and slobbering

das Geschmeide, — jewelry, piece of jewelry

das Geschöpf creature

das Geschöpfchen little creature

das Geschrei outcry, shout

geschwind quick, speedy, fast

der Gesell, -en companion, friend, fellow

die Gesellschaft society, company

das Gesetz law

das Gesicht face

gesinnt disposed, inclined

gesittet in a well-bred way; with smugly moral tone (3294)

das Gespräch conversation

gessen = gegessen eaten

die Gestalt figure; stature

gestehen admit, confess

das Gestein rocks

das Getöse din, loud noises

die Gewalt violence, power, force

gewaltsam violent

das Gewerb business, trade

gewinnen win, gain, acquire (spiritual) gain

gewiß certain, sure, assured

das Gewissen conscience

gewogen well-disposed toward, fond of

gewohnt accustomed

das Gewölb(e) vaulted ceiling, arch, dome

das Gewühl tumult

gießen, o, o pour out

das Glas glass

der Glaube faith, belief

glauben believe, have faith; think

gleich (*adv*) immediately, right away, at once, now

gleichen, i, i resemble, be equal to, match

das Glied, -er limb, member

die Glocke bell

das Glück happiness

glücklich happy

glückselig favored by fortune, lucky

glühen glow, burn, be ardent

die Glut intense heat, ardor, glow, fire

die Gnade, -n grace, mercy

gnädig merciful, gracious; gnädiger Herr Sir

das Gold gold

golden golden

gönnen (*wk*) bestow upon, vouchsafe, grant gladly, permit; nicht gönnen begrudge

der Gott God

der Götterausspruch oracle

das Götterbild divinely beautiful form; being in God's image

göttergleich divine, godlike

die **Gottheit** divinity, deity

gottlos irreligious, godless, impious

der **Gottverhaßte** one hated by God

das **Grab,** ⸚**er** grave, tomb

grad(e) straight, right, right away; just

gradehin without standing on ceremony

der **Grasaffe** young fool (*who cavorts on the green*); kittenish young person

gräßlich terrible, monstrous

grau gray, colorless

grauen grow gray (*at dawn* 4579)

grauen cause one to feel horror or dread or terror; **es graut mir** I am filled with terror

das **Grauen** dread

der **Graus** terror

das **Grausen** shuddering, shudder

greifen grasp, clutch, reach grab, seize

die **Grenze** limit, boundary, frontier

Gretchen Margaret

Gretel Margaret

Gretelchen Margaret

der **Grimm** wrath (*of God* 3800); rage (*of the Devil* 4458)

grimmig fierce, furious

–**grinsen** *see* hingrinsen

groß large, big, great, tall, grand, huge, important; **groß tun** swagger, boast, give oneself airs

der **Grund** bottom; **von Grund aus** thoroughly

grüßen give greetings to; **grüßen lassen** send kind regards

gucken peep, peek

gültig valid

die **Gunst** good will, favor

günstig favorable, propitious

das **Gut** property, piece of property

gut good; well; desirable; kind, pleasant; (*with dative*) **gut sein** be fond of, love, be well

disposed toward (3478); **recht schön und gut** very well and good

gütig amiable

die **Gütigkeit** amiability

H

das **Haar, -e** hair

haben (*wk, irreg*) have, own, possess

–**haben** *see* liebhaben

der **Häckerling** chopped straw

der **Hagestolz** bachelor

halb half; **halb und halb** more or less

halbgefault half-rotted

halblaut half aloud

halbverrückt half-crazed

der **Hals** neck

das **Halstuch** neckerchief, scarf

halt after all

halten (ä), ie, a hold, hold on to, cling to; keep house; consider; **halten für** take to be, consider; **halten von** think of; **an der ist nichts zu halten** that is of no value any more, that is of no further use (3702)

sich **halten** (ä) behave (3370)

–**halten** *see* aushalten

die **Hand,** ⸚**e** hand

der **Händedruck** handshake, pressure

handeln do business

der **Handwerksbursch** journeyman artisan

hangen (ä), i, a hang, cling

hängen hang to, cling to

sich **hängen** hang on to, attach oneself to

Hans Jack; **der große Hans** the great gentleman (2727)

Hans Liederlich a dissolute fellow, "Jack the Dissolute"

harmlos innocent

hart close

hassen hate

häßlich hateful, ugly
häufig in large numbers
das Haupt head
das Haus house, home; family; nach Haus home, homeward
das Häuschen little house
häuslich domestic, household
sich heben rise, arise, get up; hebe dich von hinnen be gone
—heben *see* aufheben
heilig holy, sacred, blessed; with holy zeal; godly (*ironic* 3040); der heilige Saint; der Heilige saint
das Heiligtum holy place, sanctuary
heimlich secret, mysterious, concealed
Heinrich Henry
heißen command; mean; call
heiter cheerful
helfen (i) help; do good, do any good
hell bright, clear
der Henker hangman, executioner
her to this place; here; come! um . . . her around
sich herablassen (ä) condescend
herankommen (ö/o) come, draw near, approach
heranzögern bring to pass through hesitation
herauf up
heraufscheinen, ie, ie shine up, cast its rays up
heraufsteigen rise, ascend
heraus out; come out!
herausführen take out, help to escape
herausheben lift out (*of the fire*)
heraustreten step out
herbei here; bring here!
herbeischaffen produce, get and bring
herbeischleichen sneak up here
herbringen bring here
der Herd hearth
herein come in! enter!

hereindringen force (its) way in
hereinkommen come in, enter, get in
hereinspringen come running in
hereintreten (i), a, e enter, step in
herführen (*wk*) lead here, bring here
herkommen come here
hernehmen (i) a, o take from
der Herr, —en, gentleman, lord, Lord, sir; Mr.; der Herr you (*respectful*); mein Herr sir; gnädiger Herr Sir
der Herrgott Lord God
herrlich splendid, glorious, lordly
die Herrlichkeit splendor, magnificence; splendid thing (2795)
hertrotten trot along
herübergehen go across; herüber und hinüber gehen go back and forth
herüberkommen come over
herübersteigen climb across
herum around, all around, around and around
herumgehen, i, a go around and around
herumspüren sniff around
herumwälzen roll from side to side
das Herz, —en heart; darling; von Herzen heartily, sincerely
herzen (*wk*) fondle, press to one's heart
der Herzensstoß thrust to the heart, mortal blow
herzig sweet
herzlich heartily, thoroughly, very, very much
heulen howl
heut(e) today; heut abend, this evening; heut(e) nacht tonight
die Hexenzunft company (guild) of witches

hie here
hier here
hierher hither, here, to this place
hierunten down here, here below
der Himmel,—heaven, heavens, sky
das Himmelreich heaven
das Himmelsangesicht lovely face (of heavenly beauty)
die Himmelsfreude heavenly bliss
die Himmelsgabe, -n gift of heaven
die Himmelsglut light (inspiration) from heaven
die Himmelsmanna manna, bread from heaven
himmlisch celestial, heavenly
hin there; go there; away, gone
hinauf up; up to
hinauflaufen run up
hinaufschicken send up
hinausschauen look out
hinbringen take there
hindern hinder
sich hindrängen yearn to be with
hinein into, go into
hineinfressen (i) eat into
hineingehen go into
hineinschielen (wk) squint in
hineintun, a, a put in
hinführen take there
sich hingeben (i), a, e surrender
hingrinsen grin away, keep on grinning
hinnen: von hinnen away, away from here
hinschmelzen (i), o, o melt into a heap
hinten back there
hinter behind
hinterdrein afterwards, along behind
hinterlassen (ä), ie, a leave as legacy
hinterm = hinter dem
hinübergehen: herüber und hinüber gehen go back and forth

hinüberschlafen (ä), ie, a die in sleep
hinunterlassen (ä), ie, a allow to go downstairs
hinunterwerfen (i), a, o throw down
sich hinwälzen writhe
hinwegraffen (wk) snatch away
hinwegtragen (ä), u, a carry off
hoch high, tall; noble, grand, important, sublime
der Hochzeittag wedding day
hoffen (wk) hope
hoffentlich I hope
die Hoffnung hope
höflich courteous
die Höflichkeit courtesy
die Höhe height; in die Höhe up
die Höhle, -n cavern, cave
der Hohn scorn, mockery
hold lovely, gentle, sweet
holen come and get
die Hölle hell
die Höllenpein agony
höllisch infernal, of hell
hören (wk) hear, listen, listen to
–hören see anhören, zuhören
der Hörsaal lecture hall
hübsch pretty, nice, fine, handsome
hülflos helpless
der Hund dog
die Hundsgestalt canine form
hungern go hungry
die Hure whore
das Hüttchen little cottage
die Hütte cottage

I

ich I
das Idol illusion, phantom, image
ihm him, it; to him; to it, for him, for it
ihn him, it
ihnen them, to them, for them
Ihr (sg) ihr (pl) you, ye

ihr her, it; to her, to it; for
 her, for it
ihr her, hers; its, of it; their,
 theirs
ihrer of them
im = **in dem**
die **Imagination** imagination
immer always, ever, still; after
 all; -ever; **nur immer** just
in in, inside, at, into
indem as, while
indes while; in the meantime
indessen while;   meanwhile;
 but meanwhile
ingrimmend spitefully, wrath-
 fully
sich **inkommodieren** go to (any)
 trouble
innen within, inside
inner inner
das **Innere** inner being; heart of
 the matter
innig deeply
ins = **in das**
das **Instrument** instrument
interessiert interested
die **Intuition** intuition
inwendig inside, behind the
 scenes
irgendwo anywhere, somewhere
 or other
irren be mistaken, err

J

ja yes
ja certainly, indeed, after all;
 be sure to; you must admit
 (*recognizing or anticipating
 agreement*)
das **Jahr, -e** year
das **Jahrtausend, -e** thousand-year
 period, millennium
der **Jammer** misery, wretchedness;
 es ist ein Jammer it's a pity,
 it's too bad
die **Jammerecke** wretched corner;
 corner of misery
die **Jammerknechtschaft** wretched
 servitude, imprisonment

je ever; **von je** always, from
 the beginning; **je . . . je** the
 . . . the (3748-9)
jeder each, every, all
jemand someone,   somebody,
 anyone
jetzt now, at present
der **Jude** Jew; Jewish moneylender
 (2842)
jung young; recent
der **Junge** boy, young chap
die **Jungfrau** maiden
jüngst recently, just recently
just just, exactly; of all things;
 really

K

kalt cold; indifferent, unfeeling
die **Kammer** room
das **Kästchen**, — little box, jewel
 casket
katechisieren (*wk*) catechize
das **Katrinchen** Katharine, Kitty
das **Kätzlein** young (tom)cat
kaum scarcely, barely; as soon
 as; **ich bin kaum alleine** the
 minute I'm alone
der **Kauz, ⸚e** screech owl; peculiar
 person
keck bold
kehren return
kein not any, none, no, not a,
 neither, no one, nobody
kennen, a, a (*wk, irreg*) know,
 be acquainted with, recognize
der **Kenner** expert, connoisseur
der **Kerker** prison, dungeon
der **Kerl** fellow
das **Kesselchen** little kettle
das **Kettchen** little chain (*jewelry*)
die **Kette, -n** chain
keusch chaste, modest
das **Kind, -er** child; girl
das **Kinderspiel, -e** child's play;
 children's game
die **Kinderwange,   -n**   childish
 cheek
kindlich childlike

die **Kirchbuße** penance done publicly in church

die **Kirche** church, Church; religion

klagen lament, complain

klang! clank!

klappen clatter

klar clear, unmistakable

das **Kleid, –er** garment; **Kleider** clothes

kleiden be appropriate for

klein small, little; petty

kling! clink! **Kling! Klang!** clink! clank!

klirren clank, rattle

klopfen: es klopft there is a knock at the door

–**klopfen** *see* anklopfen

klug sensible, clever

der **Knabe** youth; **ein braver Knabe** a fine young fellow

knarren creak

kneipen pinch, bite

kneten (*wk*) knead, mold

das **Knie, –e** knee

knien kneel

kochen cook, do the cooking

kollern roll heels over head

kommen, a, o come, come away; get; come about, happen; **ins Gerede kommen** get talked about

–**kommen** *see* ankommen, herkommen, herankommen, hereinkommen, herüberkommen, mitkommen, vorkommen

der **König** king

das **Königreich** kingdom

das **Königsmahl** royal banquet

können (a), o, o (*irreg*) be able to, can, know how to, be possible; **etwas auf dich können** be able to exert some influence upon you

der **Kopf** head

das **Köpfchen** little head, feeble intellect

der **Korb** basket

die **Kraft** power, force, strength, vigor

kränken hurt, offend, grieve

der **Kranz** garland, wreath

das **Kränzel** bridal garland

kratzen scratch

kräuseln curl, make wavy patterns in

die **Kreatur** creature

der **Kribskrabs** hodgepodge

kriechen crawl

kriegen get

die **Kröte** toad

der **Krug, ⸚e** jug, pitcher; vase

der **Krüppel, —** cripple

kühl cool

kühn bold, daring

der **Kummer** sorrow

kund known; **kund werden** come to light, become known

künftig future, coming

das **Kunststück** masterpiece, work of art

der **Kuppler** pander, pimp

kupplerisch procuring

das **Kupplerwesen** business of procuring

kurieren (*wk*) cure

kurtesieren (*wk*) court, pay court to

kurz short; **kurz und gut** in a word; **kurz angebunden** brusque, snappish; **so kurz** such a short time

der **Kurzsinn** narrow-mindedness

der **Kuß, Küsse** kiss

küssen (*wk*) kiss

L

lächeln smile

lachen laugh

–**lachen** *see* auslachen

laden load, take (upon oneself)

das **Lager** bed

–**lagern** *see* umherlagern

lahm paralyzed

lallen (*wk*) speak haltingly

das **Lämpchen** little lamp

die **Lampe** lamp

das **Land, ⸚er** land, country, district; **des Landes** in these parts (2949)

lang long; eternal; **die Zeit wird lang** time passes slowly

lang(e) long, for a long time; long ago; throughout; long since; by far (2648); **lange schon** for quite a while; **auf Zeiten lang** for quite a while (3269)

die **Länge** length; **in die Länge** all the time, day after day, for any length of time

langsam slow

längst long ago; long since

lassen (ä), ie, a let, allow; have, make (cause); see to it; leave, leave alone; stop, give up; omit; permit (to be); be becoming (3312)

–**lassen** *see* einlassen, herablassen, zurücklassen

die **Lästrung** blasphemy

lauern wait in ambush, lie in wait, lurk

–**lauern** *see* auflauern

der **Lauf** course, way

laufen (äu) run; be on one's feet (3112)

–**laufen** *see* weglaufen

lauschen listen

laut loud, aloud; audible

leben live, be alive, exist; **lebt wohl!** farewell

das **Leben** life, existence

lebendig living, alive

die **Lebensglut** glow of life

die **Lebenskraft** vital energy

leblos lifeless

ledern leather, made of leather

leer empty

leeren (*wk*) empty

legen put, lay

–**legen** *see* anlegen, niederlegen

lehren teach; tell; relate

der **Leib** body; **dir steckt der Doktor im Leib** you have the doctor in you; **dir an den dürren Leib** lay hands on your skinny carcass

leibhaftig in person; personified, incarnate

die **Leiche** body, corpse

leicht easy, easily; gentle

das **Leid** sorrow, suffering, grief

leid: leid tun make one feel sorry

das **Leiden** suffering

leiden tolerate, stand for

leider unfortunately; alas; I'm sorry to say

leidlich fairly; tolerable, sufficient

leihen, ie, ie lend (money)

leis(e) soft, quiet

lesen read, interpret

sich **letzen** enjoy; gloat

letzt last

Leute people; public

das **Licht** light; bright hue

lieb dear, beloved, sweet; precious; treasured; **lieber** rather; **Liebes** dear thing, kindness (2983); **lieb haben** be fond of

das **Liebchen,** — beloved, sweetheart

die **Liebe** love

lieben (*wk*) love; **ein Liebender** lover

liebenswürdig worthy of love; lovable, charming

die **Liebeslust** joy of love, amorous desire

die **Liebespein** torment of love

der **Liebestraum** dream (trance) of love

die **Liebeswut** frenzy of love

liebevoll loving, tender

liebewonniglich in ardent ecstasy

liebhaben be fond of

liebkosen caress lovingly

die **Lieblingsbildung** favorite shape

das **Lied,** –er song

liederlich dissolute

liegen, a, e lie; be; rest

Lieschen Elizabeth, Betty
lindern soften, calm, allay
links to the left, left
die Lippe, -n lip
die List ruse, cunning, trickery, guile
das Lob praise
loben praise, laud
der Lober, — praiser
lobesan praiseworthy; Magister Lobesan Sir Laudable
locken entice, lure; try to attract (3698)
lodern blaze, flare, be ablaze
der Lohn reward
los rid
lösen (wk) dissolve; untie, unbind, loosen
losmachen untie, unfasten
sich losmachen detach oneself, get away
sich lossprechen (i), a, o renounce
der Löwentaler, — coin (with the stamp of the Lion of Bohemia)
die Luft air; space (3572); sich Luft machen give vent to one's feelings (Trüber Tag 50)
lügen lie
das Lügenspiel illusion, phantasmagoria
der Lügner, — liar
der Lümmel oaf
die Lunge lung
die Lust desire, inclination, pleasure, joy, enjoyment; Lust bekommen feel the urge
die Lüsternheit greediness, lasciviousness

M

machen make, do; get busy; arrange, manage (things); sich groß machen begin to become large; sich Luft machen give vent to one's feelings
-machen see aufmachen, fortmachen, losmachen, vormachen

die Macht power, authority
Madam madam
das Mädchen girl, maiden, virgin
das Mädel, -s girl
die Magd girl, servant girl
das Mägd(e)lein, — (little) girl
der Magen stomach
der Magister Master of Arts
das Mal time
Malta Malta (Mediterranean island)
man one; you; people; mankind in general; we; somebody; they; (English passive)
manch many (a)
der Mann man; husband
die Mär information, news, tidings
das Märchen fairytale
Margarete Margaret
Margretlein little Margaret; Peggy
das Mark core, depth; marrow, quick
der Markt market
Marthe Martha
das Mäskchen (little) mask, visage; pretty face
die Maß: reiche Maß in full measure (3769)
Mater dolorosa (suffering mother) Virgin sorrowing at the cross
die Mauer, -n wall
die Mauerhöhle hollow place in the wall
der Mauernpfeiler, — pillar
das Maul mouth; ein schiefes Maul ziehen make a wry face
Meduse Medusa
das Meer sea, ocean
mehr more, any more
mein my, mine, of me
meinen think, believe; mean; expect (2739)
meist mostly
meisterlich masterly, like a master
die Menge public, crowd

der **Mensch, –en** man, human being, mortal, person; (*pl*) people, mankind
die **Menschenhand** human hand
die **Menschenseele** human soul
die **Menschheit** human nature, mankind
    Mephisto Mephistopheles
    Mephistopheles Mephistopheles
    merken mark, remember
die **Messe, –n** mass
der **Messerrücken** back of a knife
die **Metaphysika** metaphysics
die **Metze** hussy
die **Milch** milk
die **Missetat** misdeed, crime
die **Missetäterin** evildoer, criminal
    mißhören misunderstand, fail to hear correctly
der **Mist** rubbish, dirt, manure
    mit with, along, at, by, in company of; with it, with them (2884); come with you (4542)
    mitkommen come along; come with me
der **Mittag** noon; **nach Mittage** (this) afternoon
    mitten in the midst of; **mitten durch** right through the midst of
die **Mitternacht** midnight
das **Möbel** piece of furniture
    mögen (a), o, o (*wk, irreg*) may, be likely; can; could; care to; should like
der **Mond** moon
das **Moos** moss
    moralisch moral
der **Mord** murder
der **Mörder, —** murderer
    mörderisch murderous
    mörderlich frightful, terrible
der **Morgen** morning
    morgen tomorrow; **morgen früh** tomorrow morning
die **Mühe** labor, exertion, effort, toil

der **Mund** mouth; testimony
    munter merry, cheerful, lively
    murmeln murmur
    müssen (u), u, u (*wk, irreg*) be obliged to, have to, must, ought to, be forced to, be compelled to
der **Mut** courage; **Mut fassen** take courage
    mutig cheerful, light-hearted (3147)
die **Mutter** mother
    mütterlich motherly, in a mother's way; as mothers do
    mutwillig carefree, exuberant, roguish

N

    nach to, toward, for, in (*direction*); after; according to; **nach und nach** gradually, little by little; **nach ... zu** toward
der **Nachbar** neighbor
die **Nachbarin** neighbor
    nachsehen (ie), a, e excuse, condone
die **Nacht, ⸚e** night; **nachts** at night; **heute nacht** tonight
    nächtig nocturnal; dark, gloomy
    nächtlich nocturnal; **nächtlicher Weile** at night
der **Nacken** neck, back of the neck
    nah near, close (by)
    nähen sew
die **Nahrung** nourishment, food
der **Name, –n** name, expression; word
    Napel Naples
der **Narr** fool
das **Närrchen** little fool
die **Nase** nose; **an der Nase spüren** tell by looking at
das **Naserümpfen** turning up one's nose
    nasführen lead by the nose, make a fool of

die **Natur** nature

neben beside, next to

necken tease

nehmen (i), a, o take, take away; **sich in acht nehmen** take care, be careful (not to)

–nehmen *see* annehmen, aufnehmen

neigen bend, incline, turn

sich neigen bow, bend

nein no

nennen name, call by name, call; bring to mind

neu new; fresh

neulich recently, the other day

nicht not, nor, no; **nicht doch** Oh no; not at all

nichts nothing, not anything

nichtswürdig vile, contemptible

nicken nod

nie never, at no time

nieder down

niederlegen lay down, deliver; produce; **Zeugnis niederlegen** attest an oath, make a deposition

niederschlagen (ä), u, a cast down

niedersinken break down, collapse

niederstürzen tumble, fall heavily

sich niederwerfen (i) throw oneself down

die **Niedrigkeit** humility, lowliness

niemals never, at no time

niemand nobody, no one

nimmer never; not; **könnte nimmer** just couldn't (3498)

nimmermehr never again, nevermore

noch still, yet; nor; even; else, more, moreover; ever (so); in addition to; nor; **noch nicht** not yet

die **Not** distress, need; emergency; sorrow, care, suffering, misery, trouble, difficulty; **meine liebe Not** a great deal of trouble, a difficult time

nun now; well . . .

nur only, merely, just, simply; alone; nothing but; all but; **nur immer** just

die **Nuß, Nüsse** nut

O

o oh, ah

ob whether, if, I wonder if; **als ob** as though

oben above; **wie oben** as described earlier

die **Öde** solitude

oder or

offen open; unlocked

öffnen open, unlock

oft often, frequently, many times

ohne without

in **Ohnmacht** in a faint

das **Ohr, –en** ear

der **Ohrring, –e** earring

das **Opfer** sacrifice, offering, victim

die **Ordnung** order, orderliness

die **Orgel** (church) organ

der **Orgelton** sound of organ music

der **Ort** place; small city; spot

P

packen seize, lay hands on, get hold of

Padua Padua (*city in Italy*)

das **Pärchen** couple (in love)

parieren parry

das **Pastetchen, —** small pie, patty

die **Pein** misery, difficulty, pain, torture

die **Perle, –n** pearl

die **Perlenschnur, ⸚e** string of pearls or beads

Perseus Perseus

der **Pfaff** (pompous and arrogant) priest, cleric

das **Pfand** pledge, security, pawn
der **Pfarrer** priest, preacher
das **Pferd, -e** horse
der **Pfifferling, -e** a common mushroom; trifle, thing of no value
die **Pflicht** duty, obligation
pflücken pluck (*flower*)
pfui fie! shame!
die **Physik** physics
die **Physiognomie** physiognomy
die **Plackerei** vexation, bother, worry
die **Plage** vexation, worry
plagen bother, pester, annoy
der **Plan** plan, design, scheme
die **Planke** plank
der **Platz** place; square
plaudern chat, prattle
die **Polizei** police
die **Posaune** trumpet (of Judgment Day)
sich **prägen** (*wk*) impress itself, make an impression
-preisen *see* vorpreisen
der **Priester, —** priest, preacher
probieren test, try, try out
profan profane, secular
das **Püppchen** little doll; little darling
die **Puppe** puppet; darling
-putzen *see* aufputzen

Q

die **Qual, -en** torture, torment, agony
sich **quälen** torment oneself, worry
quillen rise; swell, grow

R

der **Rabenstein** place of execution
rächen avenge
der **Rächer** avenger, executioner
die **Rammelei** copulation, wantonness
der **Rand** edge, brink
rasch quick, rash, youthful and impetuous
ein **Rasender** madman

raten advise, suggest
der **Rattenfänger** rat catcher (*Pied Piper*)
rauben steal, deprive (of), take away
der **Rauch** smoke
raufen fight, scuffle
rauh rough; chapped
rauschen rustle
das **Recht** right, privilege
recht right, correct, proper; all right; quite, downright, thoroughly; real, really; suitable; **recht haben** be right; **recht behalten** be right, win an argument; **mit rechten Dingen** in a proper way, as it should be
die **Rede** speech, talk; words
sich **regen** move, stir; spring up, come to life; be astir; make a stir; spend a little money
Rehzwillinge (two young) roes that are twins
reiben rub
das **Reich** realm, kingdom
reich rich, abundant, full; opulent, fine
reichen present, hand; extend, give
rein pure, clean, clear; **die Reinen** pure in heart (3831); **rein halten** be a good housekeeper
reinlich neat, clean
die **Reise** journey, trip
reisen (*wk*) travel, get around; **ein Reisender** traveler, traveling man
-reisen *see* fortreisen
reißen (= zerreißen 3575) tear to pieces
die **Religion** religion, religious faith
das **Requiem** requiem, mass
retten (*wk*) save, rescue, redeem
reüssieren have luck, do well, succeed

revidieren check, inspect, survey the situation

richten (*wk*) judge; arrange (2857)

der **Richter** judge

–**riechen** *see* anriechen

der **Riegel,** — bolt

der **Ring, –e** ring

rings all around, everywhere, on all sides

ringsum all around, everywhere, on all sides

der **Ritter,** — knight

die **Ritze** crack

die **Rose, –n** rose

das **Rot** red

rot red

rücken move

rufen, ie, u call; summon, cry, say loudly

die **Ruh(e)** rest, peace, quiet; sleep; leisure (2642); peace of mind (3349, 3626)

das **Ruhebett** bed of ease (resting place = *the grave*)

ruhen rest, lie; repose

der **Ruheplatz** bed; bedroom

ruhig quiet, calm; undisturbed

rühren (*wk*) move; touch

rupfen pluck (*petals*)

S

's = es; das (3638, 4486)

die **Sache, –n** thing, object; affair

das **Sächelchen,** — pretty little thing, knicknack

der **Säckel** purse

sagen (*wk*) tell, say, talk, speak

das **Sakrament, –e** sacrament

die **Sakristei** vestry

Sancta Simplicitas (*Latin*) holy simplicity, holy innocence

der **Sand** sand; dust (*Trüber Tag* 20)

der **Sänger** singer, serenader

satt satiated, full; **sich satt weiden** feast one's eyes to satisfaction

säumen tarry, linger

säuseln whisper, rustle pleasantly

der **Schade** misfortune

das **Schädelspalten** splitting a skull

schaden do harm

schaffen get, procure, obtain; be active, work, achieve; do

–**schaffen** *see* herbeischaffen

schaffen, u, a create (3339)

der **Schall** sound

sich **schämen** be ashamed, be embarrassed

schamrot flushed (red) with embarrassment

die **Schande** shame, dishonor, disgrace

der **Schandgesell(e)** scoundrel

schändlich shameful, abominable, foul

die **Schar, –en** host, crowd, group

scharf sharp, keen

die **Schärfe** keen blade

der **Schatz** treasure; sweetheart, beloved

schaudern tremble, shiver

schauen look, gaze; see, gaze at

–**schauen** *see* hinausschauen

der **Schauer** feeling of fear and anticipation; cold shiver

schauern shudder, cause to shudder

das **Schaustück** showpiece, pocket piece; lucky coin

scheiden, ie, ie separate, part company, leave; tear oneself away

der **Schein** light, gleam

scheinen, ie, ie seem, appear

–**scheinen** *see* heraufscheinen

der **Schelm** rogue; scoundrel

schelten (i) curse; scold, denounce, call names

schenken (*wk*) grant, give, present; give presents

der **Scherben,** — flower pot

scherzen joke, have fun, sport

sich **scheuen** shun, fear, avoid, be afraid of

-schicken *see* fortschicken, hinaufschicken
das **Schicksal** fate
sich **schieben** shuffle along
schief slanting, crooked; **ein schiefes Maul ziehen** make a wry face; **es steht schief darum** something is wrong with it
-schielen *see* hineinschielen
das **Schiff** ship
ohne **Schimpf und Spaß** seriously
schimpfen scold, curse
der **Schlaf** sleep
schlafen (ä), ie, a sleep
schlagen (ä), u, a knock, smash
-schlagen *see* niederschlagen
die **Schlange** snake, serpent
schlecht bad, poor
schleichen sneak, prowl
-schleichen *see* herbeischleichen, vorbeischleichen
der **Schleier** veil
sich **schleifen** drag oneself
schlicht simple, unpretentious
schließen, o, o shut, close, lock; conclude; **geschlossen** locked in chains, fettered
das **Schloß** lock
das **Schloß** castle (2774)
-schlurfen *see* einschlurfen
der **Schluß** conclusion, end
der **Schlüssel, —** key
das **Schlüsselchen** little key
die **Schmach** shame, disgrace
schmachten languish
schmächtig languishing
schmälen criticize
der **Schmaus** banquet, feast
schmecken taste; taste good
schmelzen (i), o, o melt
der **Schmerz, -en** pain, grief, affliction
die **Schmerzenreiche** (deeply afflicted) Dolorosa
schmieden forge; weld
sich **schmiegen** nestle, cuddle
der **Schmuck** adornment, jewelry, finery

schmücken adorn, dress
das **Schmuckkästchen** little jewelry box
der **Schnee** snow
schnippisch pert
schnuffeln sniff, have one's nose (in)
das **Schnürchen** little string
-schnüren *see* zuschnüren
schon already; all right
schön beautiful, fine, handsome, fair, pretty, nice; **schön und gut** well and good
schonen spare, be considerate of
die **Schönheit** beauty
der **Schopf** forelock; **beim Schopfe fassen** seize by the hair of the head
der **Schoß** lap; **in den Schoß nehmen** take to one's bosom
schreiben, ie, ie write
schreien, ie, ie shout, cry
der **Schrein** closet, cupboard
der **Schritt** step; **Schritt und Tritt** every movement
der **Schuhu** (= Uhu) owl
schuld to be blamed, to blame
die **Schuld** guilt, fault
der **Schuldner** debtor
die **Schulter, -n** shoulder
der **Schurke** villain
schwach feeble, weak; faint
schwadronieren swagger, talk big
schwarz black, dark, sinister
schwärzen (*wk*) blacken
schwätzen babble, chatter, talk nonsense
schweben hover
-schweben *see* abschweben, aufschweben
schweifen roam, ramble; move aimlessly
schweigen, ie, ie be quiet, hush
die **Schwelle** threshold
schwer heavy; difficult, hard; grave; dire
Schwerdtlein Schwerdtlein

schwerlich with difficulty
das Schwert sword
die Schwester sister
das Schwesterchen little sister
das Schwesterlein little sister
der Schwindel dizziness
schwitzen sweat, perspire
schwören swear
–schwören *see* zuschwören
schwül sultry
sechs six
die Seele soul, mind, heart; soul
(= *individual*)
die Seelenliebe true love
der Segen blessing; beneficial quality
segnen (*wk*) bless; praise, express satisfaction with
sehen (ie), a, e see, behold, look; perceive, watch, observe
–sehen *see* ansehen, aussehen, dreinsehen, einsehen
sich sehnen yearn, long
sehr very; very much, a great deal, greatly
seicht shallow, running low
sein (ist), war, gewesen be; exist, live, be alive; happen
sein his, its
seinesgleichen the like(s) of him
seitab aside, out of the way
die Seite side
seitwärts to the side, aside; over there, on the side
selbst in person, –self; even
selig blessed; blissful
die Seligkeit happiness, satisfaction
seligmachend saving (souls), leading to heaven
der Sessel armchair
der Seufzer, — sigh
Sibylle Sibyl
sich –self, –selves; one another; each other
sicher certain, certainly; secure, safe, sure; steady

sichtbar visible
sie (ihrer, ihr) she, her, it; Sie you
sie (ihrer, ihnen) they, them
sieben seven
sieden seethe, boil
singen sing
sinken sink; fail, grow dim (2781)
–sinken *see* niedersinken
der Sinn, -e/-en sense; soul; meaning; thought; mind; idea; ihr vergehen die Sinnen she will faint, she will be confused; nach meinem Sinn according to my wishes or liking; aus dem Sinn out of mind
sinnlich sensual, sensuous
sittenreich well-mannered
sittreich well-mannered
sitzen, saß, gesessen sit
–sitzen *see* aufsitzen
so so, like that, in this manner, as, thus; then, this way; as well as; so ein such a
sogar even
sogleich immediately, directly, right
der Sohn son
solch such (a), so, of that kind, of that sort
der Soldat soldier
sollen, o, o (*wk, irreg*) shall, be to; be supposed to; should, ought to; be compelled to; be said to; Was soll's? What's up? What's the matter?
der Sommervogel, ⸚ butterfly
sonderbar strange
die Sonne sun
sonst otherwise, else, in other respects; formerly; usually
der Sophist(e) sophist
sorgen take care of; attend to one's work (3145); sorgen für look after, provide for; see to

soviel as much, so much
die Spange buckle, clasp
sparen (*wk*) save
der Spaß fun, joke; **aus dem Spaß lassen** leave unmentioned
spat late
spät late
spazieren take a walk, stroll
–spazieren *see* vorüberspazieren
der Spaziergang promenade
der Spiegel mirror
das Spiegelglas large mirror, pier glass
das Spiel play, game, sport; **ein Spiel von** at the mercy of (2724)
spinnen spin
das Spinnrad spinning wheel
spionieren (*wk*) spy around
der Spitzenkragen lace collar
der Spott mockery, ridicule
die Spottgeburt monstrosity
spöttisch sarcastic, mocking
die Sprache language
sprechen (i), a, o speak, talk; say
–sprechen *see* freisprechen, lossprechen
das Sprichwort proverb
–springen *see* aufspringen, hereinspringen
spuken haunt; **es spukt mir durch alle Glieder** I feel in my bones
spüren (*wk*) sense, feel; scent; recognize
das Stäbchen small staff, judge's wand; **das Stäbchen bricht** the rod is broken (*official signal to proceed with the execution*)
die Stadt, ⸚e city
die Stadtmauer city wall
stampfen stamp one's foot
starr fixed, staring
die Stätte place
stecken put; be hidden; **dir steckt der Doktor im Leib** you have the doctor in you

sich stecken hide
–stecken *see* einstecken
der Steg narrow wooden bridge
stehen, a, a stand, stop; be becoming (to); **was gehen und stehen mag** what is possible; **wie steht es mit** how about; **es steht schief darum** something is wrong with it; **es steht geschrieben** it is written; **Wo steht dein Kopf?** Where is your reason? **stehen lassen** pay no attention to
–stehen *see* aufstehen, dastehen
–steigen *see* heraufsteigen, herübersteigen
der Stein stone, rock
die Stelle spot, place; **auf der Stelle** instantly, on the spot; **von der Stelle** from here
stellen put, place
sich stellen place oneself; act
–stellen *see* vorstellen
das Sterbebett deathbed
sterben (i), a, o die
sterblich mortal
der Stern, –e star
die Sternblume star flower, aster
der Stich sting, prick; **im Stiche lassen** abandon, leave in the lurch
die Stichelrede, –n taunting
still quiet; **Still!** hush!
die Stille peace
das Stillschweigen silence
die Stimme voice
stinken stink; smell
die Stirn(e) forehead, brow
stolz proud, haughty; lofty
–stoßen *see* zurückstoßen, zustoßen
stracks straight, straightway
die Straße street
der Strauß bouquet
streichen stroke (3628)
sich streichen steal (3657)
–streichen *see* einstreichen
streifen roam
streuen strew, scatter

stricken knit
das Stroh straw
das Strumpfband garter
die Stube small room
das Stück, –e piece, item; in allen
  Stücken about everything, in
  every way
die Stufe, –n step
der Stuhl chair; confessional (2623)
  stumm silent
das Stündchen good little while,
  cozy hour; brief hour
die Stunde, –n hour
der Sturm storm
  stürzen fall; plunge; ins Verderben stürzen ruin
  suchen seek, look for
der Sultan sultan
die Sünde, –n sin
das Sünderhemdchen sinner's shirt
  (*worn to do penance*)
  süß sweet, charming, lovely

T

der Tag, –e day; daylight
der Tagesblick light of day
die Tageszeit daytime
das Tagewerk, –e: alle sechs Tagewerk' all creation
  täglich daily, every day
der Tanz dance
  tänzeln: tänzelnd gehen skip
  along with dancing steps
der Tanzplatz dancing place
  tapfer valiant, brave; strong,
  hearty
die Tapferkeit bravery
die Tasche, –n pocket
der Tau dew
  tausend thousand
  tausendfach thousandfold
der Teich pond
das Teil share
der Teppich cover
  teuer dear
der Teufel devil, Devil, Satan
  teuflisch devilish
  thronen sit enthroned

Thule Ultima Thule (*the north-
  ernmost part of the habitable
  world, a very distant and very
  mysterious land*)
  tief deep; heavy (sleep)
die Tiefe depth
das Tier animal, beast
der Tisch table
  toben rave, rage
der Tod death
die Todesnot death agony
der Todesschlaf sleep of death
  toll mad, absurd, wild
die Tollheit folly, madness
der Ton sound, tone; strain, tune
  tönen resound
  topp! agreed!
der Tor fool
  töricht foolish
  tot dead
  töten kill
der Totenschein death certificate
  tragen carry; wear
die Träne, –n tear
der Trank drink, potion
  tränken give to drink, nurse
der Traum, ⸚e dream
  traurig sad, dreary
  traut dear, beloved
  treffen meet; catch (3206)
  trefflich excellent, fine; very
  well
  treiben, ie, ie drive, urge; do
  treten (i), a, e enter, step; in
  die Ehe treten enter into
  matrimony; mit Füßen treten kick
  –treten *see* auftreten, eintreten,
  hereintreten, vortreten, zurücktreten
  treu faithful, honest, loyal
die Treue fidelity, faithfulness, loy-
  alty
der Trieb urge, desire, impulse
  triefen drip
  trinken, a, u drink; fill with
  water (2779)
der Tritt step; Schritt und Tritt
  every movement

der **Tropfen,** — drop
trösten console
trüb gloomy, clouded
Trümmer ruins
trutzen bid defiance
tugendlich virtuous
tugendreich virtuous
tun, a, a do, make, perform,
  effect, act; **tät(en)** did (*with
  an infinitive, as an auxiliary
  of a past tense*)
-tun *see* hineintun
die **Tür(e)** door
die **Türbank** bench in front of the
  house door
das **Türchen** small door
türkisch Turkish
der **Türner** keeper, warden
die **Tyrannenart** way of tyrants

U

übel evil, bad; **übel dran sein**
  be badly off; **Übel's** bad
  things, anything bad; **es soll
  ihr übel gehen** she's in for a
  bad time
über over, above; about
überall everywhere, in all
  places
überallmächtig omnipotent
überdringen, a, u overpower;
  descend upon
der **Überdruß** weariness, more than
  enough
sich **überessen (i), a, übergessen**
  overeat, gorge oneself
überfließen, o, o overflow
übergeben (i), a, e hand over
sich **übergeben (i), a, e** surrender
**übergehen: die Augen gingen
  ihm über** his eyes filled to
  overflowing (*with tears*)
überirdisch supernatural, spiritual, heavenly
**überlaufen (äu): mich über-
  läuft's** a cold shiver comes
  over me
übermächtig most powerful, im-
  mense

übermannen overwhelm
übermorgen day after tomorrow
übern = über den
übernehmen (i), a, o take upon
  oneself
überschnappen snap,   crack;
  break down
übersinnlich metaphysical;
  "platonic"
überstehen endure, survive
übersteigen overflow
überwinden conquer, overcome
übrig left over; **alle übrigen**
  all others; **im übrigen** as for
  the rest, otherwise
übrigbleiben remain, be left
um around, about; at; for; in
  order; **um und um** all
  around, everywhere
umbringen, a, a (*wk, irreg*)
  kill
umfangen (ä), i, a surround,
  encompass
umfassen embrace, encircle
umgeben (i) surround
umherblicken look around
sich **umherlagern** take up positions
  round about
umherspazieren (*wk*)   stroll
  around
umhüllen envelop
umnebeln surround with a
  haze
ums = um das
umsonst gratuitously, for nothing, free
unanständig unbecoming, im-
  modest
unaussprechlich inexpressible
unbehaust homeless
und and; **und wär' ich noch so
  fern** no matter how far
  away I might be
unendlich infinite, unending,
  endless
unerträglich unbearable
ungefähr about
das **Ungeheuer** monster

ungeleitet

ungeleitet unescorted, by oneself
ungerecht unjust; wrongly
acquired (2823)
das Unglück bad luck, misfortune
unglücklich unhappy
unhold ill-disposed, ungracious
der Unmensch brute, monster
unnütz useless
das Unrecht wrong, injustice
unruhvoll restless
die Unschuld innocence
unschuldig innocent
unselig unfortunate
unser our, ours; of us
unsereins one of us; we
unsichtbar invisible
unten below; downstairs
unter under, below; among
sich unterfangen (ä), i, a venture
untergraben undermine
unterhalten (ä) entertain
unterm = unter dem
sich unterstehen dare, presume
unterweil now and again;
meanwhile
unterweisen instruct
sich unterwinden venture, make
bold to
das Untier monster
unwiederbringlich irreparable
unwissend ignorant

V

Valentin Valentin
der Vater father; Father
der Vätersaal ancestral hall
der Väterthron grandfather's chair
verbergen (i), a, o hide, conceal; verborgen secret
sich verbergen (i) hide
das Verbrechen crime
verdauen digest
das Verderben destruction, ruin
verderben go to perdition, be
destroyed
verdrießen annoy, trouble; dis-
courage

verflucht accursed, confounded,
damned
verführen (wk) seduce; mis-
lead
vergällen (wk) make bitter,
turn into gall
vergangen past
vergeben (i), a, e forgive
vergebens in vain
die Vergebung forgiveness, remis-
sion
vergehen swoon; die; melt
away; pass
vergessen (i), a, e forget
das Vergnügen pleasure, delight;
amusement
vergraben (ä), u, a bury
vergriffen well-worn
verhallen die away
verhaßt hated, hateful, odious
verheimlichen (wk) conceal
verirrt lost, gone astray
verkehren (wk) turn
der Verklärte, -n Blessed Soul
(*one transfigured after rising
from the grave*)
verkürzen shorten
verlangen desire
das Verlangen desire
verlassen (ä) abandon, leave
die Verlegenheit -en embarrassment
verlernen (wk) forget
verliebt in love; infatuated
verlieren, o, o lose; verloren
geben give up for lost, give
up hope for
der Verlust loss
vermaledeit cursed, con-
founded
das Vermögen fortune; estate
vermögen (a) be able to, be in
a position to, can
vernehmen (i), a, o hear
verpuffen set off like fireworks
verräterisch treacherous
verrucht infamous, atrocious
verrückt crazy; crazed, deranged

sich **verschieben, o, o** get out of place

verschmähen (*wk*) scorn, reject, jilt

verschwemmen (*wk*) wash down

verschwinden, a, u disappear; pass away

versehen (ie), a, e take care of

versetzen (*wk*): **den Atem versetzen** take (one's) breath away

versinken, a, u sink; be swallowed

sich **versitzen** waste one's life in idle sitting

versprechen (i), a, o promise

verständig intelligent, sophisticated, smart

sich **verstecken** hide

verstehen understand

das **Vertrauen** confidence

verworfen infamous; cast out

verzagen grow despondent

verzeihen pardon, excuse, forgive

das **Verzeihen** pardon

verzetteln (*wk*) squander

verzweifeln despair

die **Verzweiflung** despair

viel much, many, a great deal, a great number

vielleicht perhaps, maybe, perchance; by any chance

vier four

vierzehn fourteen

visieren (*wk*) look around

das **Vöglein** little bird

das **Volk** people; crowd

voll full, complete; full of; **voller** full of

vollbringen, a, a (*wk, irreg*) complete, accomplish, finish

vom = von dem

von from, of, by, about

vor before, in front of, for, on account of; ago; in preference to; **vor der Stadt** (just) outside the city

vorbei past, along; come along! over and done with

vorbeigehen, i, a walk past

vorbeischleichen, i, i move stealthily past

das **Vorhängel** small curtain (*at a peep window*)

vorkommen appear, look, seem

sich **vorlügen** falsely imagine

vorm = vor dem

vormachen: was vormachen contrive some (plausible) explanation

vornehm grand, genteel; elegant, lordly

das **Vornehmtun** superior airs

vorpreisen, ie, ie praise publicly

sich **vorstellen** imagine

der **Vorteil** advantage

vortreten (i) step forward

vorübergehen walk past

vorüberspazieren promenade past

die **Vorwelt** former age, former generation(s)

vorzüglich principally, chiefly

W

wachen be awake, sit up waiting; watch, be on guard

wachsen (ä) grow, increase

der **Wächter, —** watchman, night watchman

wackeln wag loosely, shake

wacker valiant, brisk, stalwart

wagen venture, dare

der **Wahn** false or fantastic notion, fanciful idea; delusion

wahr true, real

wahren keep for oneself

währen last, keep on

wahrhaftig truly, really, indeed

die **Wahrheit** truth

wahrlich truly, honestly, in truth, to tell the truth

der **Wald,** ⁻**er** forest, wood
das **Waldvögelein** forest bird
die **Walpurgisnacht** (*night of April 30–May 1, occasion of the annual witches' convention*) –**wälzen** *see* herumwälzen
die **Wand,** ⁻**e** wall
der **Wandel** walk; (way of) life
 wandeln change, transform
das **Wandern** wandering, travel
der **Wandrer** wanderer
die **Wange** cheek
 wann when
 warm warm
 warten (*with gen*) wait for
 warum why, for what reason
 was what, whatever; why; **was für (ein)** what kind of, what a! (2709); (= **etwas**) something, anything; somewhat
der **Waschtrog** washtrough
das **Wasser** water
der **Wassersturz** waterfall
 weben weave; make; float; hover
 wechseln (*wk*) exchange
 weder neither; **weder ... noch** neither ... nor; **weder ... weder** neither ... nor
der **Weg** path
 weg away, gone; **hier weg** away from here
 weggehen, i, a go away
 weglaufen (äu) run away
 weh(e) alas; woe, woe is; **weh tun** hurt; **wie weh(e) wird mir** how heavy with woe my heart becomes (3603–4)
 wehren prevent
das **Weib,** –**er** woman; wife
 weichen, i, i retreat; **weichen von** shun
 weiden graze
sich **weiden** feast, feed; gloat
 weihen dedicate, consecrate
 weil because, since
die **Weile: nächtlicher Weile** during the night
 weilen linger, stay; be

der **Wein** wine
 weinen weep, cry
der **Weise,** –**n** wise man, sage, philospher
die **Weisheit** wisdom
 weissagen foretell; hint at
 weit far; far away
 weiter farther, further
 welch which, what, what a, which one
 welk withered, dried
 welsch French, Italian
die **Welt** world, life
 wenden (*wk*) turn, bend
sich **wenden** turn
 –**wenden** *see* abwenden
 wenig little, small, few; scarcely; **weniger** less
 wenigstens at least
 wenn if, when, whenever; **wenn auch** even if, even though; **als wenn** as if
 wer who, whoever; someone, anyone
 werden (i), a/u, o become, come to be, develop; be; will/shall; be (*passive*); **werden zu** change into
sich **werfen** (i) throw oneself
 –**werfen** *see* hinunterwerfen, niederwerfen
der **Wert** value, worth
 wert worthy, worth; dear, esteemed; **wert sein** deserve
das **Wesen** being; nature
 wider against; **wider mich** in spite of everything I can do (3797)
 widrig unpleasant, repulsive; hostile
 wie how; as; like, as if, such as; when; **wie viel** how much, what
 wieder again, once more
 wiederkehren return, come back again
 wiederkommen come back, return
 wiedersehen see again; **Auf**

Wiedersehen Good-bye, Au revoir
sich **wiedersehen** see each other again
die **Wiege** cradle
wiegen rock (to sleep), lull
wieso how so? what do you mean?
wild wild
der **Wille** will, wish
willkommen welcome
der **Wind, –e** wind
winden twist, writhe
winken beckon, signal, nod
winterlich wintry
wir we
die **Wirtschaft** establishment, household
–**wischen** *see* abwischen
wissen (ei), u, u (*wk, irreg*) know, know how to, be informed
der **Witz** wit; good sense
wo where, wherever; if, when
woanders elsewhere
das **Wochenblättchen** (weekly) newspaper of a small town
wohin to where, whither, where, wherever
wohl well, in good health; carefully; indeed, probably, presumably; to be sure, I dare say
sich **wohlbehagen** feel comfortable
wohlgemessen fair
wohlgeweiht duly consecrated
wohltun, a, a do good, benefit
wohnen live
sich **wölben** arch
die **Wolke, –n** cloud
wollen (i), o, o (*wk, irreg*) wish, be willing, desire; be about to; allege, claim to; **wir wollen** let us; **wollte nicht** just wouldn't
die **Wonne** bliss, rapture, ecstasy
der **Wonnegraus** ecstatic dread, dreadful ecstasy
wonniglich rapturous

das **Wort, –e** word, saying; promise
wühlen burrow; rage
–**wühlen** *see* durchwühlen
wunderbar amazing, strange
der **Wunsch** wish
würde(n) would
würdigen (*wk*) deign
das **Würfelspiel** dice game
der **Wurm** worm
das **Würmchen** poor little thing
wüten be furious, rage, be violent

Z

zagen be afraid, be faint-hearted
zählen (*wk*) count, take a census
zahm tame; not belligerent, not quarrelsome
der **Zahn, ⸗e** tooth
zappeln (*wk*) writhe, twitch, kick convulsively
zart tender, delicate, soft, gentle
das **Zauberbild** image produced by magic
der **Zauberduft** magic fragrance, magic haze
die **Zauberei** witchcraft, sorcery
der **Zauberfluß** magical stream
das **Zauberpferd, –e** magic horse
zaudern hesitate, be irresolute
die **Zeche** revel; **auf der Zeche** charged against one
der **Zecher** reveler
zehren gnaw, consume
–**zehren** *see* aufzehren
die **Zeit, –en** time, age; **in Zeiten** betimes, in good time; **auf Zeiten lang** for quite a while
zeitig early
der **Zeitvertreib** fun, amusement, pastime; **zum Zeitvertreib** to pass the time
zerbrechen (i) break
zerfließen melt away
zerreißen, i, i tear to pieces

zerschmettern shatter, smash

zerstreuen (*wk*) scatter

die Zerstreuung, –en distraction, diversion

zerstückt distracted

der Zeuge, –n witness

das Zeugnis testimony; certificate

ziehen, o, o draw; move; ein schiefes Maul ziehen make a wry face

–ziehen *see* aufziehen

ziemlich fairly, rather; so ziemlich rather (3119); fairly well (3371)

die Zier ornament, adornment

zieren adorn

das Zigeunerwesen gipsy doings

das Zimmer room

die Zither cittern, lute, guitar

zittern tremble, quiver

–zögern *see* heranzögern

der Zopf, ⁓e braid

zu to, in; at; along with; in order; too

züchtig decorous

zucken move jerkily, twitch

zücken move swiftly

zudrücken press shut

das Zufallswörtchen casual word

die Zufriedenheit contentment

der Zug, ⁓e: in letzten Zügen with his last gasp, in his last moments

zugehen happen; es geht zu things go; es geht nicht mit rechten Dingen zu there's something wrong about this, things like this don't happen by proper means

zugleich at the same time

zugrunde gehen be ruined, be destroyed

zuhören (*wk*) listen to

zuliebe as a favor, to please (*someone*)

zum = zu dem

die Zunge tongue

–zupfen *see* abzupfen

zur = zu der

zurichten (*wk*) prepare (*as one prepares a dainty dish*)

zurückelassen (ä) let out again

zurückgeben give back, return

zurückstoßen (ö), ie, o repulse

zurücktreten (i) step back

zusammenschmeißen smash to bits

zusammenstürzen descend, fall crushingly

zuschnüren lace up; **schnürt mir das Innere zu** ties me all up inside

zuschwören swear to

zustoßen (ö), ie, o attack, lunge (*in a swordfight*)

zwar to be sure; I admit; of course

der Zweck aim, purpose, goal

zwei two

das Zwillingspaar pair of twins

sich zwingen zu press toward, press to

der Zwinger enclosed space adjacent to the city walls